how to service
TAPE RECORDERS

how to service
TAPE RECORDERS

C. A. TUTHILL

HAYDEN BOOK COMPANY, INC., NEW YORK

PREFACE

Magnetic recording was invented in 1898. However, it was not until World War II that instruments of this type became sufficiently practical and low in cost to be suitable for home use. General public acceptance began in the early 1950's, and today there are available for general use over 200 models of tape recorders produced by over 70 manufacturers.

These models include portable units ranging from pocketsized economy models for use by reporters and salesmen through heavy-duty, professional-quality instruments for use by explorers and anthropologists under the most rugged field conditions. They also include a full selection of home models ranging from economy units for recording domestic events and radio and TV programs, and costing well under $100, through recorders costing over $1,000 and capable of producing stereophonic sound of professional quality. Also included is a good selection of tape recorders and associated equipment designed specifically for educational uses.

Operating according to the same basic principles, but incorporating highly-specialized electronic and mechanical variations, are the recorders used for TV broadcasting, computer applications, military uses, and storing and transmitting information from the vast variety of instruments employed in space vehicles.

Because of this widespread use of tape recorders, radio and television servicemen are frequently being asked to repair and maintain these complex electromechanical devices. Experience in troubleshooting radio and TV sets is a valuable asset in maintaining tape recorders. However, these instruments are so different in electronic arrangement and include so many complex mechanical assemblies that servicemen cannot maintain them effectively without a good understanding of their basic principles and common variations. Many laymen, experimenters, and high-fidelity enthusiasts are also interested in the principles and details of magnetic tape-recording machines and would like to become capable of using this information to maintain their own equipment.

This book was written with the requirements of these widely divergent users in mind. It presents, in a balanced manner, an introduction to the basic principles of magnetic recording, a detailed analysis of the operation of the mechanical and electronic systems in a wide selection of modern tape recorders, and detailed directions for maintenance and troubleshooting. The original edition, published in 1954, has been almost totally rewritten to incorporate information concerning present-day machines.

Grateful acknowledgement is made to various manufacturers and distributors for generously making available information and illustrations on tape recorders of their manufacture or supply. As far as practicality has allowed, credits have been given in the text and illustrations. Because only a small portion of the supplied material can be credited in so specific a manner, the author wishes to thank all those who contributed:

Allied Radio Corp.; American Elite, Inc.; Ampex Corp.; Amplifier Corporation of America; Armour Research Foundation; Audio Devices, Inc.; Bell Sound Systems, Inc.; Bell Laboratories, Inc.; Berlant Associates; Brush Development Co.; Concertone Div., Astro-Science Corp.; Eico, Electronic Instrument Co.; General Industries Co.; Heath Co.; Inter-Mark Corp.; International Radio & Electronics Corp.; Robert C. Merchant; Radio Corporation of America; Sony Corp.; Stancil-Hoffman Corp.; Star-lite Electronics Corp.; Superscope, Inc.; Tandberg of America, Inc.; Tandbergs Radiofabrikk; Telectro Industries Corp.; Telefunken; Viking of Minneapolis; V-M Corp.; Webster Electric Co.; Westinghouse Electric Corp.

The author also wishes to express his gratitude to Seymour D. Uslan for his help in editing this book and to Nathan Buitenkant for his extensive assistance in collecting informaton concerning present-day tape recorders and in updating the previous edition.

C. A. TUTHILL

CONTENTS

Chapter 1

INTRODUCTION

The magnetic tape recorder has contributed a new and superior method of recording to the field of communications, a method far more flexible and economical than any heretofore known. The impact and importance of tape recorders is demonstrated by their acceptance by all major television and radio broadcast stations, the major recording and motion picture studios, Military Services, and hundreds of manufacturers both here and abroad.

This development did not come about by accident; it is founded on the many outstanding advantages which tape recording offers over other recording methods. That tape sound-quality excels, that expensive processing is not required, that playback is immediately available, and that tapes may be erased and used over and over again at no additional cost, are all factors which have helped to establish tape as the champion in the sound recording field.

The economy of tape recorders, both in construction and use, is perhaps their most outstanding characteristic. Despite their high quality of reproduction, tape machines require far less power than other types of recorders. Furthermore, tape recorders are readily portable, since their construction requires a minimum of weight. Thus, on-the-spot scenes can be recorded for later reproduction, a facility which is constantly used by all radio broadcasting companies. Besides remote pickup recordings, many major radio and TV shows are taped prior to broadcasting. By editing and correcting the show during production, a finer show results without regrettable and costly mistakes on the air. Editing of programs is rapid and easy, requiring but a pair of scissors and tape for splicing. Amateurs, too, make wide use of this flexibility. Beyond this convenience, the greatest economy is derived from the erasure feature, which permits a single tape to be erased and reused hundreds of times. Considering all these factors, the rapid growth of commercial, military, and amateur markets for tape recorders is readily understandable. Thus, with the introduction of tape recording, a truly new business with a growing future and an excellent career incentive has arrived almost overnight.

1

Origins and Development

The idea of magnetic recording is not new. In 1898 the first magnetic recording machine, the *Telegraphone,* was patented by Valdemar Poulsen, the "Edison of Denmark". However, Poulsen's initial efforts were not followed immediately by much further progress; the sound quality then obtained was poor, and the process little understood.

In December 1907, Mr. Poulsen and his colleague, Peder Oluf Pedersen, were granted a patent in the United States; this patent described a direct-current "bias control" which represented some improvement. (The meaning of *bias control* is explained in Chapter 3.) Working in the U.S. Naval Research Laboratory, W. L. Carlson and G. W. Carpenter were granted a patent in August 1927; they described an *alternating-current bias control* which resulted in a greatly improved quality of recording. Up to that time, however, only wire and steel tapes had been used as a recording medium.

One of the first devices to introduce paper and plastic tapes coated with powdered magnetic substances was the German *Magnetophon,* demonstrated in 1935. Although the quality of reproduction from early plastic tapes was inferior to that then obtained from steel tapes, the obvious potential economic gains created sufficient interest to promote a rapid development of this new medium.

The major evolution of modern paper and plastic base tapes was first seen at a demonstration in 1937, by Mr. C. N. Hickman of the Bell Telephone Laboratories. At this demonstration, *vicalloy* was introduced as a new coating for nonmagnetic tapes, and Hickman's magnetic tape recorder offered an excellent quality of reproduction.

Both foreign and domestic capital quickly became interested in this convenient, economical method of recording, and a potentially enormous amateur market for home recording paralleled commercial possibilities. Soon the Armour Research Foundation in Chicago developed a means to bond a magnetic sound track upon motion-picture film; when the Eastman Kodak Company signed a license agreement with the Foundation, another high-potential market was opened.

Applications

Today there are literally thousands of commercial and military uses for magnetic tape recorders, many of these uses being far more exacting in frequency response than is the human ear. The Military Services use tape recordings for training programs, for recording the results of complex computing machines, telemetering, and a host of applications. In industrial research applications, test data may be recorded having an ultrasonic frequency spectrum (beyond 20,000 cycles per second) or a direct-current response. The recording of pressure, temperature, and other slowly varying quantities necessitates these d-c responsive tapes.

On the other hand, the recording of an extremely wide frequency band, far beyond that required by sound, has also been mastered. Most

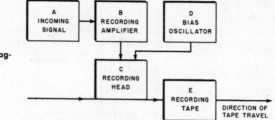

Fig. 1-1 Block diagram of magnetic-recording process.

major television programs, both in black and white and in color, are now prerecorded on magnetic tape, saving tremendous sums over those required for motion-picture film recordings. These amazing feats are made possible only because ultrasonic frequencies may be recorded and reproduced by the magnetic tape process. Discussions of these techniques, however, exceed the scope of this book, which has been purposely limited to the field of sound recording.

Besides the unusual applications, tape recorders find increasing acceptance in many everyday sound-recording applications. Tape recorders have become an indispensable part of educational programs, and are in daily use in universities and schools throughout the world. The American University in Washington, D. C. has used repetitive and selective reproduction of tape recordings in foreign language studies for several years. Such "electronic language laboratories" are also in great favor in Georgetown University's Institute of Languages and Linguistics, at Louisiana State University, Cornell University, and many others.

The Tape Recording Process

The underlying physical process which makes magnetic tape recording possible is essentially very simple. The sounds to be recorded are converted into corresponding variations of an electric current. In turn, this varying electrical current induces variations of a magnetic field in a coating of tiny magnetic particles, which are bonded to a narrow strip of tape. The magnetic field variations force the magnetic particles to move to new positions on the tape, in accordance with the strength of the field at each point on the tape. Once moved, these particles remain stationary, and a magnetic record is the result.

Based on this magnetic action, a practical tape recorder performs three essential functions: *recording, reproduction,* and *erasure.* The method of accomplishing these three basic functions will now be briefly explained.

Recording. (Refer to the block diagram, Fig. 1-1.) A low-level incoming audio signal (block *A*), corresponding to the sound variations to be recorded, is introduced to the recording amplifier (block *B*). The signal is electronically amplified in the recording amplifier and then fed to the recording head (block *C*).

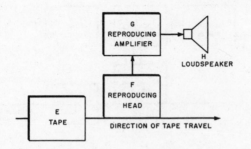

Fig. 1-2 Block diagram of magnetic-reproducing process.

As stated earlier, a *bias control* proved to be the crucial factor responsible for high quality of the recorded signal. This bias control is derived from a bias oscillator (block *D*) and is combined with the amplified audio signal at the recording head (block *C*).

The recording tape (block *E*) is in contact with and drawn across the recording head (block *C*). The combined functions of units *A, B, C, D,* and *E* make possible magnetic tape recording. These basic units are explained in detail in Chapter 3.

From the foregoing it becomes evident that some mechanical device must be employed to draw the tape across and keep it in contact with the recording head. These complex devices are known as *tape transport* or *tape drive* mechanisms. Thorough acquaintance with the functioning of these mechanisms is essential to the operator of tape machines (examples are discussed and illustrated in Chapters 5 and 6).

Reproduction. As in other forms of recording, making a record is only the first step; reproduction calls for a second magnetic process. The magnetic record preserved on the surface of the tape must in some way be scanned magnetically, and then amplified for audible reproduction.

Refer now to the block diagram of Fig. 1-2. During reproduction the tape (*E*) is in contact with and travels past a reproducing head (*F*). The speed and direction of travel must be the same as used during the recording process. The fixed magnetic pattern upon the tape then induces voltage variations in the windings of the reproducing head, these voltages varying in accordance with the recorded pattern of coated

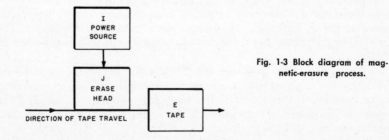

Fig. 1-3 Block diagram of magnetic-erasure process.

particles on the tape. The resulting signals are amplified by the reproducing amplifier (G) and are made audible through a loudspeaker (H). Thus reproduction is essentially a reversal of the recording process. Note one important feature: a magnetic recording may be played back immediately after it is recorded; no further processing of the record is required.

Erasure. Any magnetic recording may be erased from the tape and the same tape reused hundreds of times. However, erasure calls for a third magnetic process: a magnetic field of considerable magnitude is applied to the tape to erase the record. (Fig. 1-3 illustrates magnetic erasure in block diagram form.)

A power source (I) energizes an erase head (J). A magnetic field of great intensity is produced by this erase head while the tape (E) is in contact and drawn past it. The erasure field then overpowers the recorded pattern of the aligned magnetic particles coated on the tape, and all particles are reoriented by the field, coming to rest in random positions. This action results in complete erasure, leaving the tape ready for a new recording.

The important fact to note is that all three of these processes, *recording, reproduction,* and *erasure,* depend entirely upon magnetic action. Because of this, the next chapter is devoted to a review of basic magnetism with an emphasis on characteristics applicable to tape recording.

The block diagrams (Figs. 1-1 through 1-3) include the basic components necessary for tape recorders. However, additional refinements are required in practical units. During the recording process, low-level incoming signals must be amplified, equalized (that is, frequency-compensated) and controlled against the possibility of overload or inadequate signal level (this is true of all recording methods). Equalization is again necessary during reproduction. An overall picture of a magnetic recording system including these additional refinements appears in Chapter 4, and circuit details are analyzed and illustrated in Chapter 6.

Chapter 2

BASIC MAGNETIC PRINCIPLES

For the purposes of this book, a discussion of basic magnetic principles need only concern the atoms, comprising material, and their *magnetic moments*. We will also consider the individual *domains* within the structure of all magnetic materials, including recording tape.

Atoms, Electrons, and Domains

All atoms contain minute negatively charged particles called *electrons*. Within each atom these electrons move in orbits around the heavier nucleus, and at the same time each electron (and each nucleus) spins about an axis of its own. Such a moving or spinning electron constitutes an electric current, and an electric current produces a *magnetic field*.

In the crystals of highly magnetic substances, each atom has more electrons spinning in one direction than in the other. Throughout a minute sub-crystalline region called a *domain*, containing about 10^{15} atoms, these uncompensated spins are all in the same direction. Within such a *domain* the spinning electrons produce an intense magnetic field. Thus, each individual domain may be considered a tiny magnet having a north and a south pole. When such a tiny magnet is placed within a magnetic field it tends to align its north-south pole axis with the direction of the field. The turning force, or torque, with which this alignment takes place is called the *magnetic moment,* and is proportional to the pole strength and the distance between the poles.

Thus the domains within a crystal of a magnetic substance, such as iron, are all individually magnetized, but these tiny domain magnets point in all conceivable random directions. With such unoriented domains, the individual magnetic (turning) moments cancel each other out, and no external magnetism is exhibited (see Fig. 2-1A). When an outside magnetizing force is applied these individual magnetic domains align themselves more and more in the direction of the applied field, and their individual magnetic moments begin to add up. When the substance becomes completely magnetized (or *saturated*) all the domains are aligned with the direction of the field, and all the magnetic moments add up to a powerful magnetic force (Fig. 2-1B).

Magnetization and Magnetic Properties

The relative ease with which the alignment of the domains takes place determines a material's magnetic properties. For example, in iron this alignment is easily effected, hence iron is highly magnetic; on the other hand, steel requires a more intense field to produce a given degree of magnetization, because its domains become aligned with greater difficulty. When the magnetizing force is withdrawn, however, the domains of steel *remain* aligned, while those of soft iron return largely to their former random positions. Therefore, although hard to magnetize, once magnetized, steel retains its magnetism and is called a *permanent magnet;* soft iron can be magnetized easily, but only temporarily while being exposed to an outside magnetizing force. Even in soft iron, however, some *residual magnetism* remains after the magnetizing force is withdrawn.

All the *ferromagnetic* materials, such as iron, are easily magnetized. Non-ferromagnetic materials, such as chromium, either cannot be magnetized at all or magnetized only to a slight degree. Briefly, the reasons for these differences have to do with the crystalline and atomic structure of materials; the type of crystal structure, the atomic behavior, and the spin orientations of the electrons are among the important factors. Even ferromagnetic substances show a great decline in their magnetic characteristics when alloyed with other elements. For example, an alloy comprised of 0.3% carbon, 10% manganese, 6.5% nickel, and the balance iron, proves to be non-magnetic at room temperature (the magnetic properties of many materials are highly dependent on temperature).

Magnetic Characteristics

One way of finding out the magnetic characteristics of a material is to magnetize it. When a known magnetizing force (symbol H) is applied to a material, the resulting induced magnetization or *flux density* (symbol B) can be measured and recorded. As different values of the magnetizing force (H) are applied to the material, the resulting

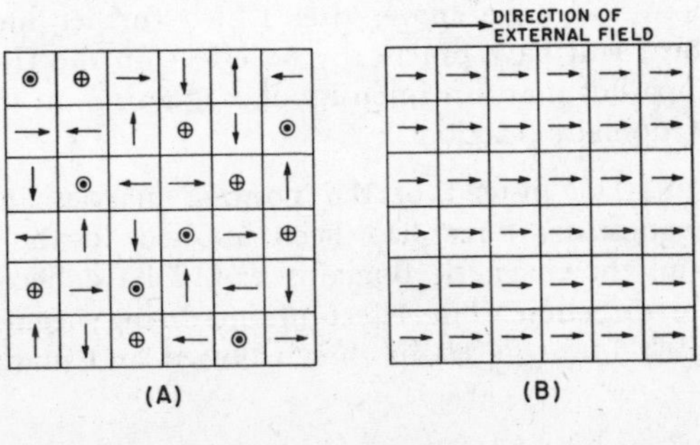

Fig. 2-1 (A) Domains have magnetic moments in all possible directions in an unmagnetized iron crystal; (B) Domains are aligned in the same direction when the iron is fully magnetized.

(A)   (B)

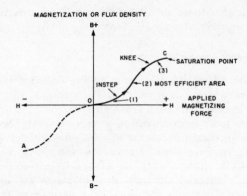

Fig. 2-2 Magnetization curve for iron.

flux densities (B) can be plotted, resulting in a characteristic magnetization curve which is of great importance to design engineers. Such a magnetization curve for iron is shown in Fig. 2-2. The explanation for the peculiar shape of the curve may be summarized as follows:

1. When a small but gradually increasing magnetizing force (H) is applied to unmagnetized iron, the domains affected by the force increase slightly in size, at the expense of adjacent unaffected domains. This results in a small amount of magnetization of the iron, which increases uniformly with increasing values of H. The portion of the solid curve (Fig. 2-2) where this occurs is marked (1).

2. As the applied magnetizing force is increased a sudden and more forceful change in the orientation of domains occurs. During this action the magnetic flux density (B) per unit of force applied, increases at a greater rate than discussed in the paragraph above. This portion of the ascending curve is marked (2) in the figure. Being the most efficient operating portion of the curve, it is used for most magnetic devices, including tape recorders.

3. As the magnetizing force is increased still further, the slow orientation of the remaining unaligned domains takes place, in the portion of the curve marked (3). Only a minute increase in flux density now results as shown by the "knee" in the curve, and the material is said to be magnetically *saturated*. Full saturation is actually reached at point c on the curve, after which further increase in the magnetizing force will have practically no effect on the flux density. From this it is apparent that full intensity of magnetization is a function of the volume of domain reaction.

4. If instead of the positive magnetizing force (H), a negative magnetizing force had been applied to the unmagnetized sample of iron, the magnetic domains would have become aligned in the opposite direction. The effect of increasing negative values of the magnetizing force $(-H)$ is shown dotted and marked OA in Fig. 2-2.

5. The average slope or steepness of the magnetization curve (that is the ratio $\frac{B}{H}$) is a measure of the ease of magnetization of the material, and is called *permeability* (symbol μ).

Hysteresis

When the iron whose magnetization curve is shown in Fig. 2-2 is for some reason demagnetized, the magnetization curve is not retraced; but a second curve *cdef* (Fig. 2-3) is established with higher values of flux density for corresponding values of the magnetizing force. (The broken magnetizing curve *oabc* in Fig. 2-3 corresponds to curve *oc* in Fig. 2-2.) As the value of the magnetizing force (H) is decreased, it is found that the flux density (B) does not decrease as rapidly, as shown by the left-hand curve (*cde*) of Fig. 2-3. This characteristic lag of the flux density behind the magnetizing force is called *hysteresis*. When the magnetizing force decreases to zero, the flux density still has a positive value (*od*); that is, the iron remains to some extent permanently magnetized. The value of the flux density where the descending curve cuts the axis (at point *d*) is called the residual or *remanent* flux density (B_r) of the material. It is the value obtained when H equal zero again.

If the magnetizing force H is now increased again in the *negative* direction, the flux density B becomes zero for a certain value (*oe*) of the magnetizing force, called the *coercive force* (H_c). The characteristics of remanence and coercive force are of great importance in determining the performance of magnetic recorders.

Hysteresis Loops. When the negative magnetizing force is further increased to a negative maximum (*of*), numerically equal to the positive maximum, then reduced to zero and again raised to the original positive maximum, the graph traces through points *e, f, g, h,* and joins up with the original curve at point *c*. The closed curve, formed for one complete

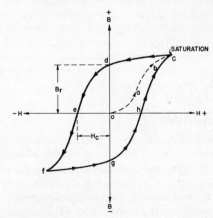

Fig. 2-3 Hysteresis loop for a complete cycle of the magnetizing force.

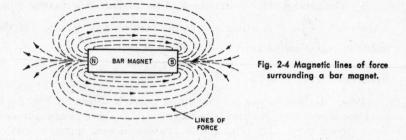

Fig. 2-4 Magnetic lines of force surrounding a bar magnet.

cycle of the magnetizing force (with an alternation in each direction), is called a *hysteresis loop*. The area inclosed within the loop (*cdefghc*) represents a measure of the energy lost as heat (the friction overcome in aligning the domains in one complete cycle of magnetization. It is important to remember that the values of B on the descending (left-hand) curve are greater than those on the ascending (right-hand) side of the curve *fc*.

Hysteresis loops cannot be expressed in analytical form, hence graphical representations, such as Fig. 2-3, must be used for calculations. The values of remanence and the coercive force are not a definite property of a particular magnetic material; the shape of the curve and the values of B_r and H_c depend on the magnitude of the positive and negative maxima of the magnetizing force and on whether the substance was originally unmagnetized. For different conditions a whole family of hysteresis loops may be produced, all more or less similar to Fig. 2-3. In the illustration only one magnetic cycle has been analyzed; in practice, however, the current in an a-c electromagnet alternates very rapidly, and the magnitude of the current, and hence the magnetizing force H, may vary over a considerable range of values. If the magnetizing force reaches different maxima during the hysteresis cycle (because of current variations), minor hysteresis loops are traced out within the main loop. Such minor loops occur when an a-c bias is applied to a tape during recording, as explained in Chapter 3. Hysteresis plays an important part in tape recorders; as the currents within the magnetizing coil of the recording head vary in amplitude, hysteresis losses in the form of heat are produced, and affect the magnetic field about the poles of the recording head.

Magnetic Fields

Interactions between magnets can be explained if we assume that there are centers of force at the poles of such magnets. Consider, for example, a permanent magnet consisting of a simple straight bar. It has a *north pole* of a certain strength at one end of the bar (the north-seeking end), and a *south pole* of equal strength at the other end of the bar. As is apparent from the field of force surrounding this bar magnet (Fig. 2-4), the north and south poles act as centers of force; for practical purposes the rest of the magnet can be ignored. The law of force found between a north and a south pole, either of the same magnet or of two different magnets, is comparable to the inverse square laws which hold for gravitation and electrostatic charges. Briefly it may be stated as:

The force between two magnetic poles is proportional to the product of their pole strengths and inversely proportional to the square of the distance between them. The force results in attraction if the poles are unlike (north and south), and results in repulsion if the poles are alike. This may be expressed mathematically, for two magnets placed in a vacuum or in air, as:

$$F = \frac{m \times m'}{d^2}$$

where F is the force between the poles in dynes; m and m' are the pole strengths of the two magnets, respectively; and d is the distance between them in centimeters. This law must be modified by a multiplying con-

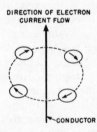

Fig. 2-5 Circular magnetic field around a conductor, through which electrons flow in the direction indicated.

DIRECTION OF ELECTRON CURRENT FLOW

CONDUCTOR

stant, to take into account the characteristics of the medium, if the two magnets are not in a vacuum or in air.

The pole strengths (m and m') in the above equation are measured in *unit magnetic poles*. This unit is defined as having a strength or force of one dyne upon an equal pole when placed 1 centimeter away from it in a vacuum or in air.

When a magnet of pole strength m is placed in a magnetic field of strength H it experiences a force $m \times H$ in the direction of the field (that is, tangent to the lines of force). This important relation can be expressed quantitatively as:

$$F = m \times H$$

where F is the force in dynes, m the strength of the magnet in unit poles, and H is the field strength measured in *oersteds*.

Demagnetization

When a bar of iron is magnetized longitudinally by placing it in a magnetic field, it develops a north pole at one end and a south pole at the other end (Fig. 2-4). If a unit north pole is placed externally near the center of this bar magnet, the attraction of the south pole of the bar magnet and the equal repulsion of its north pole will urge the unit north pole toward the south pole of the magnet, or in a direction opposite to that in which it is magnetized. If this external unit north pole were introduced *within* the bar magnet, it would still experience a force urging it in the direction of the south pole of the bar magnet. Although it would be unable to move, this opposing force of the unit north pole would produce a magnetic field within the bar opposite in direction to the original field of magnetization of the bar. Such an opposing field, which tends to weaken the original magnetization, is called *demagnetization*. The stronger the opposing field, and the shorter the bar in comparision to its cross section, the greater this demagnetizing effect would be. This demagnetizing effect is of considerable importance in magnetic tape recording, as will be explained in Chapter 3.

Permanent Magnets

Permanents magnets of horseshoe or ring shape are sometimes used for the erasure of magnetic recordings. The materials used for permanent magnets have one common characteristic: the magnetic moments of their domains cannot be easily disturbed, nor easily reoriented. Therefore, the initial magnetization of these materials requires the application of high magnetizing field strengths, but once magnetized these materials keep their magnetic strength. This characteristic of permanent magnets to hold their magnetization, once acquired, is called *retentivity*.

The stability and retentivity of *Alnico* magnets (consisting chiefly of aluminum, nickle and cobalt) is noteworthy. Demagnetization from any but the most powerful strays fields will scarcely affect Alnico. The performance of permanent magnets also depends to a great extent on the structure and magnetic characteristics of their air gaps, which will be discussed later on in the chapter.

Magnetic Effect of Electric Currents

When a current flows through a wire or other conductor a *magnetic field* is set up, thus any conductor carrying current radiates a magnetic field of its own. If a magnetic compass is carried around a vertical wire, as shown in Fig. 2-5, it will be found that the magnetic field is circular about the wire at any point along its length. As shown here, when the electron current flows upward, the north-seeking pole of the compass needle will always point in the clockwise direction of the electron flow while the compass is moved around the wire (in this book, electron flow is assumed, rather than conventional current flow). Should the direction of the electron flow be reversed, the compass behavior will also reverse. The strength of the magntic field around the wire diminishes as the distance from the wire increases. When the electron flow through the wire is constant, the magnitude of the magnetic field also remains constant.

The intensity of the field at any point near the wire may be expressed in oersteds, and is:

$$H = \frac{I}{5 \times r}$$

where H is the field intensity in oersteds; I is the current flow in amperes; and r is the distance from the axis of the wire in centimeters.

Solenoids. If the wire is formed into a loop and the electron flow is constant in one direction (Fig. 2-6A), the lines of magnetic force will all point in one direction with respect to the axis of the loop. When several loops form a coil (Fig. 2-6B), the lines of force passing through the center of the coil will all be aligned in the same direction, thereby creating a field of greater intensity than that surrounding a single loop. A north and south pole will appear at opposite coil ends; the polarity is determined by the direction of the winding. A still greater magnetic field intensity would be obtained were an iron core to be inserted into the coil. When the strength of the current flowing in the coil increases or decreases, the intensity of the magnetic fields varies accordingly. Within such a coil (called a *solenoid*) the intensity of the magnetic field is given by the equation:

$$H = 1.257 \times I \, n$$

where H is the field intensity along the axis of the solenoid in oersteds; I is the current in amperes; and n is the number of turns per centimeter of length of the solenoid.

Strictly speaking, this relation gives the magnetic field intensity at the center of a solenoid. At each of the ends of a long solenoid so much of the magnetic flux has leaked out around the sides that the field intensity is only one-half of that given above.

Electromagnetism

When an iron core is inserted partially or wholly into the center of a solenoid, as shown in Figs. 2-7 (A) and 2-7 (B), the number of lines of force within the coil is greatly increased, because the iron core offers much less resistance to the flow of magnetic lines of force than does air. Flux lines will traverse the iron core in preference to air, even though the core may be partially outside the coil. As an example, Fig. 2-7 (A)

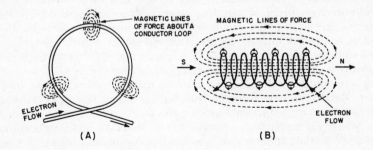

Fig. 2-6 (A) Magnetic lines of force about a conductor loop; (B) Field around a coiled current-carrying conductor.

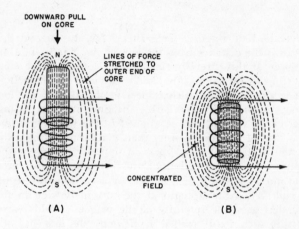

Fig. 2-7 Solenoid with an iron core, partly inserted in (A), and wholly inserted in (B).

shows the lines of force stretched out like rubber bands. Such "stretching" causes a pull upon the iron core, tending to drag it into the coil; when the field is sufficiently great the core will be entirely drawn into the solenoid. Such units are called *electromagnets* and are often employed to actuate direct-current solenoid-plunger switches and circuit breakers in tape recorders. The electromagnets are energized when a current is switched on and create a magnetic field within the solenoid.

In accordance with the equation for solenoids, it will be found that as the current in the coil of an electromagnet is doubled its magnetic intensity is doubled. If the number of turns in the coil is doubled, the magnetic intensity is once more doubled. From this we conclude that the flux density or magnetic intensity of an electromagnet is proportional to the product of the current, in amperes, and the number of turns of the coil.

Permeability. Electromagnets may be operated by direct current or by alternating current of any frequency, such as audio or higher frequencies. In fact, the flux emanating from the poles of a tape recording head is controlled directly by the audio-frequency signal voltages applied to the winding of the head. A magnetic material having high permeability is desirable for an electromagnet, so that the applied magnetizing force and the volume of the material may be held within practical limits. Relatively pure iron, or iron having a low silicon content, is generally used in laminated form for the core structure of electromagnets. Where extremely high permeability is desirable, nickle-iron alloys, such as *Permalloy, Hipernik,* or a nickel-iron-copper alloy called *Mumetal,* are often used.

In some communication components, and particularly in recording heads, extreme stability of permeability is required throughout the working range. A nickle-iron-cobalt alloy known as *Perminvar* (meaning: permeability invariable) and a nickle-iron alloy called *Copernik* possess this property at relatively low flux densities. Unfortunately their permeability is low, but they have the unique properties of negligible residual magnetism and of negligible coercive force throughout their useful range of permeability.

Comparison of Magnetic and Electric Circuits

Magnetic and electric circuits have both differences and similarities. The electrical conductivity of a material has no relationship to its magnetic permeability. Air, a poor conductor, also has low permeability, in the order of 1/10,000 that of ferromagnetic materials. Bismuth, a good electrical conductor, is the most diamagnetic substance known, having a permeability nearly equal to that of air.

The resistance that a material presents to magnetic flux (this resistance is called *magnetic reluctance*) depends primarily upon the material and dimensions of the *magnetic circuit* in which it is placed. *Reluctance* is directly proportional to the length of the magnetic circuit (measured in the direction of flux) and inversely proportional to its cross-sectional area. Reluctance limits the quantity of magnetic flux in the magnetic circuit, being somewhat similiar to the resistance of electrical circuits. However, while the resistance of an electrical circuit does not (ordinarily) depend on the current flowing through this circuit, the reluctance of a magnetic circuit *does* depend to some extent on the flux density already established in the circuit.

Ohm's Law in Magnetic Circuits. The rules for applying Ohm's law to series and parallel *magnetic* circuits are the same as for applying Ohm's law to series and parallel electrical circuits. As has previously been explained, the value of the fraction B/H (that is, the ratio of the flux density to the magnetizing force) is called the *permeability*. The inverse of that ratio (H/B) is called the *reluctivity* of the material, and corresponds to the form of Ohm's law. Thus we have:

$$\text{Reluctivity} = \frac{1}{\text{Permeability}} = \frac{H}{B}$$

As mentioned, the *reluctance* depends on the length of the magnetic circuit and its cross section:

$$\text{Reluctance} = \frac{\text{Reluctivity x Length}}{\text{Area of cross section}}$$

The magnetizing force H (often called *magnetomotive force*) may be visualized as being similar to electric voltage, while the flux density B resembles the electric current.

Care must be exercised, however, against over-confident use of analogies between magnetic and electric circuits. The resistance of a certain copper wire may be 10.4 ohms per milfoot regardless of how many amperes are flowing through it. The reluctance of standard silicon steel, however, may be 0.0025 per cubic centimeter when only four flux lines are threading each square centimeter of the steel, while this same steel

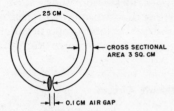

Fig. 2-8 Ring magnet with air gap.

may have a reluctance of only 0.00014 when its magnetic flux is increased to 7,000 lines per square centimeter. For this reason, standard values are not used for the permeability of these materials when magnetized to various degrees.

Air Gaps

When an air gap is introduced in series with a magnetic circuit, a great increase in the reluctance of that circuit results. This situation prevails, for example, in a magnetic recording head. Consider the example illustrated in Fig. 2-8; here an iron core has a cross-sectional area of 3 sq. cm; the length of the path within the core is 25cm; and the length of the air gap is 0.1cm. Assume the permeability of the iron ring to be 500. What is the total reluctance of the path?

$$\text{Reluctivity} = \frac{1}{\text{Permeability}}$$

$$= \frac{1}{500}$$

$$= 0.002$$

$$\text{Reluctance (of iron)} = \frac{\text{Reluctivity x Length}}{\text{Area of Cross section}}$$

$$= \frac{0.002 \text{ x } 25}{3}$$

$$= 0.0167$$

$$\text{Reluctance (of air gap)} = \frac{1 \text{ x } 0.1}{3}$$

$$= 0.0333$$

Hence the total reluctance of the magnetic circuit equals 0.0167 plus 0.0333 or 0.05. (The determination of the actual flux distribution in the air gap, and of the fringing and leakage losses caused by the air gap, is an analytical problem beyond the concerns of this book.)

Magnetic Shields

It is sometimes necessary to prevent the flow of magnetic lines of force through certain components in a system. A magnetic shield, such as that shown in Fig. 2-9 may then be introduced. In this case, a ring-type magnet is surrounded by an iron cover, which serves as a magnetic shield. The leakage flux lines surrounding the magnet follow the path of least reluctance, which is provided by the iron shield, and do not penetrate through the outside of the shield.

Magnetic shielding is generally applied to the recording and playback heads of a tape recording system. These heads must be adequately shielded against magnetic interaction between heads, as well as from the influence of external fields. When permanent-magnet type erase heads are used, magnetic shielding becomes imperative.

Soft-Iron Poles

A horseshoe or a ring-type magnet consisting wholly of one kind of material may not provide the specific flux pattern in and around its air gap which is best suited to a certain function. In such cases, correction and shaping of the flux pattern is sometimes achieved through the introduction of tapered soft-iron pole pieces (Fig. 2-10). The tapered poles offer a greater concentration of flux density across the air gap.

Fig. 2-9 Magnetic shield around ring-type magnet, showing leakage path.

A MAIN MAGNETIC PATH
B LEAKAGE PATHS
C MAGNETIC SHIELD
D AIR GAP

Electromagnetic Induction

Faraday discovered that a current is *induced* in an electric conductor which is placed into a varying magnetic field; that is, a field in which the number of magnetic flux lines change with time. This effect can be produced in a variety of ways, some of which are:

1. An alternating current constantly reversing its magnetic field (the resultant variations induce a current in a conductor placed within that field).

2. Moving a magnet relative to a conductor, or vice versa (so that a current is induced in that conductor).

3. Closing or opening a d-c current (if the source of the magnetic field is a direct current, a voltage will be induced in a conductor, placed within that field, at the instant when the direct-current circuit is closed or opened).

The effect of inducing an electromotive force (emf) into a conductor through the action of a magnetic field is called *electromagnetic induction*. There are but three conditions required to generate an induced voltage. These are: (1) a magnetic field, (2) the presence of a conductor within that field, and (3) motion between the conductor and the

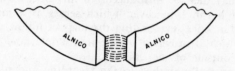

Fig. 2-10   Permanent Alnico
magnet with tapered soft-iron
poles.

field. When this induced voltage gives rise to a current through a closed circuit, it may be said that a current has been induced, although actually only a voltage can be induced.

The overall concept of electromagnetic induction is clarified in Lenz's law which states in effect: Whenever a current is established in a circuit by an induced emf through motion in a magnetic field, its direction is such that the magnetic field set up by the resulting current tends to oppose the motion which produced it.

The direction of an induced voltage is given by Faraday's law, which states: The emf induced in a circuit equals the negative of the rate of increase of flux through that circuit.

Conductor Moving in a Magnetic Field

The four parts of Fig. 2-11 illustrates these laws; (A), (B), (C), and (D) progressively analyze the result of moving a conductor in a magnetic field. Part (A) shows a conductor at rest in a fixed magnetic

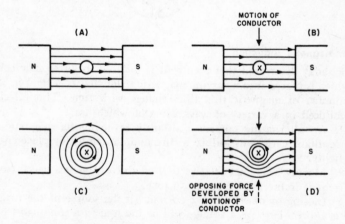

Fig. 2-11 Conductor moving in a magnetic field (A, B, C, and D). In (A) the conductor is at rest in the magnetic field; in (B) the conductor is pushed downward, inducing an electron flow which is directed into the page; (C) the field produced by the current-carrying conductor; (D) the composite magnetic field of the magnet and the conductor. A counter force is developed tending to push the conductor against the original motion.

field, established between the north and the south pole of a magnet. In this case no current flows through the stationary conductor. In (*B*) an external mechanical force is applied to push the conductor downward. This motion causes an electron flow in the conductor which is directed into the page, as indicated by the *X* across the conductor.

Part (C) shows the direction of the field around the conductor resulting from the electron flow through it (any conductor carrying a current has a field of its own, as previously explained). The induced field is counter clockwise around the conductor (for clarity, the magnetic field between the poles of the magnet is not shown).

In part (*D*) the resultant action is shown. The lines of flux between the magnetic poles and those of the field about the conductor become additive in such a manner that a stronger field is produced below the conductor than above it. Above the conductor the magnetic flux lines are weakened as they clash with the opposing-direction flux lines produced by the conductor. Because of this, the conductor opposes the original motion and tends to be pushed upward.

Induction. The same phenomenon occurs when current flows through one of two conductors placed parallel to each other. In the case of direct current no induction will take place, except at the instant when the current is either turned on or off. However, when an alternating current flows through one conductor, its lines of force will expand from it as the current rises in magnitude during one half-cycle. This, in turn, initiates an induced current in the second conductor, which flows in a direction opposite that of the current in the first conductor. For the second half-cycle, the conditions for each conductor will become reversed.

Similarly, a coil of wire subjected either to flux lines from a magnet, or coupled to a field of flux produced by another coil, will have a voltage induced in its winding.

Chapter 3

MAGNETIC RECORDING

All magnetic recording systems embrace three magnetic processes: recording, reproduction, and erasure. Each process will be discussed separately, with a natural emphasis being placed upon recording. Erasure is also of prime importance, however, being possible only with the magnetic method of recording. Any strip, section, or entire reel of magnetically recorded tape, wire, or film, may be erased *on the spot* by demagnetization.

The tape may then be reused immediately as virgin or neutral tape for further recordings. Since this cycle may be repeated almost indefinitely, erasure alone is a powerful economic factor in favor of magnetic recording.

Thus, in this chapter the three magnetic processes are discussed and various early methods are also taken into account, because techniques now considered obsolete may prove highly useful in the future. At the present time there are three established methods of magnetic recording; these are: perpendicular, tranverse, and longitudinal.

Perpendicular Recording

Perpendicular tape recording was first attempted years ago; in this method tape is used which has previously been magnetized to saturation. The saturation flux is applied at right angles to the motion of the metallic tape surface, as shown in Fig. 3-1. One side of such a tape then has a north polarity and the other side a south polarity, such tape is a permanent magnet in strip form. When subjected to audio-frequency modulation, this saturated tape has its magnetic pattern disturbed and finally aligned laterally across its surface. Such a polarized tape, passed between two diametrically opposed perpendicular pole pieces (P1 and P2 in Fig. 3-1) and subjected to a modulating flux, is capable of recording only positive half-cycles; changes in sign of the modulating signal are suppressed, because of the polarization of the tape, resulting in a highly distorted record. However, wider frequency response for a slow tape speed is still claimed by exponents of this method, which is rarely used at the present time.

20

Transverse Recording

Figure 3-2 shows an arrangement for transverse recording, in which the poles are placed at opposite edges of a saturated tape rather than perpendicular to its surface. This method also utilizes magnetically saturated tapes. In this case, however, the recording flux is spread across the width of the tape. One major difference between transverse and perpendicular recording is the greater distance between recording head poles in the transverse recording. As a consequence transverse recording requires a greater magnitude of the modulating signal.

Longitudinal Recording

In longitudinal recording magnetization is paralled to the motion of the tape. This method, used almost universally today, seems to be the only practicable one for *wire* recording, where there is bound to be a certain amount of twisting of the circular wire as it passes the pole pieces. Present-day longitudinal magnetization is produced in the recording tape by passing it over the pole pieces of a ringhead magnet having a gap perpendicular to the motion of the tape. However, there are two older methods of longitudinal magnetic recording which are also presented here, for reference. One is accomplished with a single pole piece (Fig. 3-3A) while the second utilizes two poles staggered laterally in relation to the tape (Fig. 3-3B). (Tape travel is from the left to the right of the page in all examples shown.)

1. *Single Pole-Piece Longitudinal Recording.* Assume that the tape has been previously magnetized (saturated) and that the pole piece $P1$ in Fig. 3-3 (A) emits a steady flux in the direction indicated by the arrows. Although at point 2 flux emitted from the pole will be perpendicular to the tape, at points 1 and 3, and throughout most of the area of travel past the pole, flux will be parallel to the motion of the tape. From the direction of the arrows in Fig. 3-3 (A) note that the elements of the tape approaching the pole piece are first subjected to flux 1, which approximated the same direction as the residual magnetization of

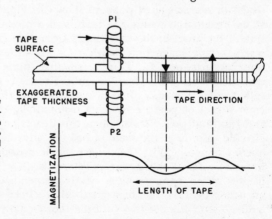

Fig. 3-1 Arrangement of pole pieces for perpendicular magnetization, and magnetization pattern resulting from audio modulation of a saturated steel tape. Courtesy: *Bell Labs, Inc.*

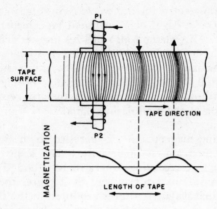

Fig. 3-2 Transverse magnetization of steel tape. Courtesy: Bell Labs, Inc.

the tape. This being true, no appreciable change in tape magnetization takes place. Directly opposite the pole the tape receives flux *2*, perpendicular to its travel. When the same tape elements reach point *3* they encounter a flux in direct opposition to the residual magnetization within the tape and also in opposition to flux *1*. This results in partial erasure of flux *1*. If we had only flux *3*, a modulating signal superimposed upon the steady flux of the pole piece could be induced in the tape with little distortion. However, because of the presence of flux *1* and *2*, interactions occur, giving rise to distortion. Such interactions are still present to some degree in modern magnetic recorders.

2. *Staggered Double-Pole Longitudinal Recording.* In contrast to the case discussed above, flux will not spread so freely if the tape is subjected to two staggered poles, as shown in Fig. 3-3 (B). Assume that residual magnetism within the tape is in a direction opposite to the motion of the tape. In this case flux *1* from pole *P1*, has little effect upon residual tape magnetism. With two poles present, the tape elements must also pass pole *P2*. Thus we see that flux *4* is perpendicular to the saturated tape, while flux *5* is in a direction opposing that of the residual tape magnetism. It is evident that any impression upon the tape from flux *3* of pole *P1* becomes distorted by the opposition of flux *4* and flux *5* of pole *P2*. Although this distortion is greater than for single-pole recording, the method has the advantage of an improved frequency response. With the staggered-pole method, longitudinal magnetization occurs at the longer wavelengths (low frequencies), while the magnetization becomes more nearly perpendicular for the higher frequencies, because the demagnetization effect at shorter wavelengths tends to steer lines of flux into the shortest possible paths. (This is discussed more fully later in this chapter.)

rapidly for a time with an increase in flux, but that with the onset of saturation the slope of the curve tapers rapidly.

With such a characteristic, small signals at the toe of the curve are recorded weakly, while strong signals in the central slope are recorded relatively stronger. Audio signals, therefore, suffer waveform distortion because of the non-linear shape of the curve.

Unbiased Characteristic. Let us assume that a magnetic recording is made under the conditions shown in Fig. 3-8; here a completely demagnetized tape is used and no bias control applied. By drawing the input signal waveform along the *B*-axis, the resulting recorded waveform can be plotted along the *H*-axis of Fig. 3-8. The resultant record is seen to have a high content of harmonic amplitude distortion because of the severe curvature of the magnetization curve. In addition, the introduction of complex input waves would produce intermodulation between various frequencies comprising the complete signal. Sum and difference frequencies, created by intermodulation, will result in further distortion.

The drastic limitations of this early method of magnetic recording without bias control was the reason for the slow development of magnetic recording until various methods of bias control were introduced.

For an analogy, the reader might look up a typical curve for an early unbiased vacuum tube and reflect on its distortion. It was found that by applying a bias voltage to the grid, the tube could be operated on a linear portion of its characteristic curve with resulting low distortion. A similar step is taken in tape recording.

D-C Bias Control

In early steel-tape magnetic recordings several methods were tried to achieve linearity. One of the first, introduced many years ago by

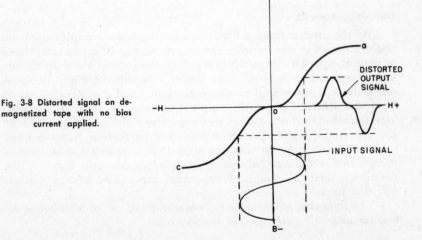

Fig. 3-8 Distorted signal on demagnetized tape with no bias current applied.

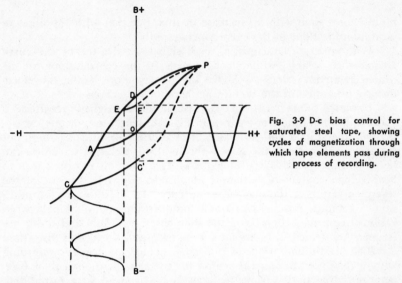

Fig. 3-9 D-c bias control for saturated steel tape, showing cycles of magnetization through which tape elements pass during process of recording.

Poulsen, consisted of a *d-c bias*. A d-c bias field of approximately 125 oersteds was applied to the recorder head winding, and an audio signal was superimposed upon this steady field. Fair linearity of magnetic recording resulted when the controlled bias *steered* the signal modulation to a straight line sector of the hysteresis curve, such as point *A* of Fig. 3-9. Since only one-half of the characteristic magnetization curve was used in this method, only low levels of modulation in the narrow straight-line sector of the curve were obtained. The noise level was high because of the steady state of magnetization resulting from the d-c bias. A previously saturated steel tape was used, saturation (point *P* in Fig. 3-9) sometimes being attained through inclusion of polarizing poles.

High-Frequency Bias

At the present time, a high-frequency a-c bias is employed to aid transfer of audio signals from the recording gap to an unmagnetized or neutral tape. The frequency of this *bias carrier* is far above audibility, usually upward from 30 kc. The simple schematic of Fig. 3-10 shows one method of applying the audio input signal and the inaudible signal from the ultrasonic bias oscillator simultaneously to the recording head (several other methods appear in Chapter 6). The term *bias* has been applied to the high-frequency carrier as a hand-down from vacuum-tube bias control. When the bias magnitude is properly controlled, a straight-line recording characteristic results, as shown in Fig. 3-11. In the figure, modified values of remanence are plotted against applied magnetic force.

The following generalizations concerning the use of high-frequency bias for magnetic recording can be made:

1. The recording characteristic is especially linear in the vicinity of the origin; that is, for small values of H.

2. The range over which linearity can be obtained is greater than for any other method of bias control.

3. The frequency of the high-frequency component is not especially critical. In fact, audible frequencies in the order of 1 kc or less will straighten the recording characteristic (but cannot be used, of course, since they would be heard).

In practice, the frequency of the ultrasonic bias carrier is several times greater than the highest frequency to be recorded; it varies from about 30 kc to 150 kc.

Theories. There is still some divergence in the theories advanced for explaining results obtained with high-frequency bias control. One reason is the complex magnetic influence a tape experiences as it traverses the recording-gap area. Another reason is the change of normal induction values due to demagnetization forces. The overall complexity is aggravated by the self-demagnetization factor occurring within the tape coating. Nevertheless, it has been accepted by all that the use of ultrasonic bias causes improved linearity, lower distortion, and reduction of noise produced by the tape.

Demagnetizing Force. As with other methods of magnetic recording, one of the most important factors effective during the process of recording with a high-frequency bias control is the resultant demagnetizing force and its effects on a recorded tape. The upper limit for maximum tape flux density after the tape passes the recording gap is determined by the value of remanent magnetization (B_r) for the tape. This upper limit is realized only at long signal wavelengths (low frequencies). As the signal wavelength is decreased (the frequency increases), surface poles along the tape exert a greater demagnetizing influence and the final flux density is reduced. In other words, the higher the signal frequency the greater the reduction of recorded signal amplitude, due to demagnetization effects, after the tape leaves the recording gap. Naturally, this effect is especially prominent at the ultrasonic bias frequency. Once the tape passes the recording gap, considerable demagnetization occurs at the bias frequency.

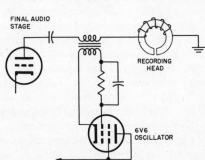

Fig. 3-10 Typical method of applying audio and high-frequency bias signal to recording head. *Courtesy: Brush Development Co.*

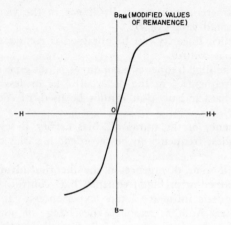

Fig. 3-11 Straight-line recording characteristic resulting when high-frequency bias is used. Courtesy: Armour Research Foundation

Optimum Bias. Tests have proved that there is a critical value of optimum bias for any specific type of recording tape. It has been further demonstrated that a slight change of bias value is necessary when different types of magnetic heads are used. Essentially the optimum value of bias is that value which eliminates the bend of the characteristic curve at the intersection between B and H (see Fig. 3-8). The straightened curve of Fig. 3-11 is obtained when the proper bias is applied. Too great a bias results in two effects:

1. The slope near the origin of the curve becomes greater than shown in Fig. 3-11, resulting in a larger output.
2. Partial erasure, due to increased bias, reduces the total effective length of the curve.

As a direct result of these two effects, excessive bias produces an increase of distortion and reduces the permissible level. In some cases, the bias value which produces the greatest output level is double the *optimum* value required for the least distortion. Even at optimum bias values a slight amount of erasure occurs, but the effect is only of consequence to the higher audio frequencies, which begin to "roll off" above 4,000 cps. From the above facts, the importance of accurate bias adjustment for specific requirements becomes evident.

Summation. Thus far we have established that:

1. Controlled application of high-frequency bias minimizes distortion during magnetic transfer of signals from recorder to tape.
2. Demagnetization within the tape introduces non-linear frequency response and losses in final signal amplitude.
3. Inherent tape characteristics also contribute to non-linearity.

Obviously, the non-linear frequency response must be compensated for. This is achieved through electronic "equalization" during recording (*pre-emphasis*) and additional compensation during reproduction (*post-emphasis*); commercial methods of accomplishing this are given in Chapter 6.

Demagnetization

Because of the effect of *self demagnetization* and tape motion away from the polarizing field, the tape elements experience a decrease in field strength and hence in remanent induction (along the upper curve, point C to point D in Fig. 3-9). Note that point D is reached when the applied field (H) is zero. Assume initially that no signal is impressed (H = 0). In counteraction, the d-c bias current produces a flux at the recording head poles which is opposite in sign to the saturating flux previously induced in the tape by the polarizing or saturating poles. This biasing action brings the magnetic operating point of the tape down to point A when no signal current is present. Tape travel away from the recording head reduces the magnetic tape induction to zero. This tape motion is represented in the hysteresis loop by portion A to O, thus completing one magnetic cycle (O to P to D to A to O).

The presence of an applied signal, during the time when the tape contacts the recording head poles, reduces tape magnetism only to point D (Fig. 3-9), instead of down to point A when the flux produced by the incoming signal opposes the fixed bias flux. In contrast, when incoming signal flux and bias flux are additive, tape magnetization is reduced to point C. For these two cases the elements retain a value of magnetic induction corresponding to E' and C', respectively. These two points represent the amplitudes of the alternating signal recorded. This method, then, makes it possible to record over a far greater portion of the characteristic magnetization curve than is possible with no tape saturation.

Magnetic Recording Tapes

From the days of Poulsen's early discoveries until about 25 years ago, magnetic wire or steel tapes served as the magnetic recording medium. (Cold-rolled carbon, chrome, and tungsten steels were among the first materials tried.) The magnetic and processing limitations of steel tapes, and their slow speed of travel, were responsible for the poor results obtained. Even today the performance of magnetic recording equipment is determined to a great degree by the characteristics of the recording tape. Metal tapes still serve specific functions where editing and splicing are not necessary. Some commercial and military machines still employ stainless steel tapes because of their durability. Among commercial examples, vending machines, advertising devices, and announcing-repeater systems may be mentioned. The stronger steel tapes are still employed in some military devices and high-speed calculating machines, such as computers and analyzers; in these, breakage is practically eliminated. Coin-operated instruments, business office equipment and sales campaign devices also frequently employ steel tapes. When the critical requirement is large output rather than wide-band frequency response, the greater thickness of the active magnetic material inherent in metal tapes is a factor favoring their use.

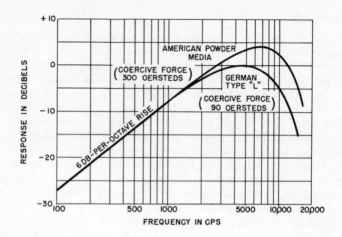

Fig. 3-12 Comparison between early type of German plastic and a later sample of American plastic tape.

Plastic and paper tapes of 10 years ago offered a choice ranging from the highly-coercive black oxide to the older low-coercive red oxide, used in World War II by the Germans. This made it necessary to adjust the bias each time that the type of tape was changed. Most modern tapes employ brown oxide, made by using a warm air blast to oxidize chemically precipitated black oxide. Now, magnetic properties of nearly all tapes are approximately similar; different brands can be interchanged freely without major changes in performance. However, bias should be adjusted to optimize performance with any favorite make and type.

Tape Comparisons. Two early German tapes used red iron-oxide (Fe_2O_3) as the active magnetic material (coating). These tapes were $\frac{1}{4}$-inch in width and 1.6 mils in thickness. One (type L) was an impregnated material consisting of equal weights of polyvinal-chloride and Fe_2O_3. The second (type LG) had a polyvinal-chloride base 1.2 mils thick. The base was coated to about 0.7 mil with 90% Fe_2O_3 plus 1% vinyl chloride in a tetrahydro-furane solution. The intrinsic coercive force of the first tape (type L) was about 90 oersteds (see Fig. 3-12) while that of type LG was about 80 oersteds. Type L had a residual induction of 100 gausses as against 550 gausses for type LG. The particle size for either tape was less than 1 micron, or 0.039 mil. The *signal-to-noise ratios* of the L and LG tapes were about equal, in commercial use a value of 65 db was attained.

Modern plastic tapes employ magnetic particles of 1 micron or less in size; these particles are mixed with a resin-binder complex that attaches them to the base material in a 0.00005-in layer. Coercivity ranges from 200 to 300 oersteds. Retentivity varies between 800 and 900 gauss. Standard reel sizes, lengths, and base thicknesses are listed in Table 4-1, at the beginning of Chapter 4.

Modern production of coated tapes has reached such stability that an output level deviation of not more than 1 db can be expected between two reels, manufactured on a production-line basis of thousands of miles of plastic tape every week. A high order of homogeneity is maintained throughout a reel of virgin tape.

Modern domestic tape bases have a certain *limpness* to provide for easy alignment around the magnetic heads. This assures uniform recording and playback levels, particularly at the higher audio frequencies. Furthermore, a minute amount of lubrication is applied to tapes to augment their smoothness and limpness. Through this treatment a ripple-free transit over the magnetic heads is assured.

Tape Characteristics. Recording tape characteristics depend upon the composition, homogeneity, and thickness of the coating upon the tape. This coating possesses two magnetic qualities, *remanence* and *coercive force,* both of which have been explained previously.

Remanence controls the signal output of a tape at the lower audio frequencies, whereas coercive force provides a measure of attainable tape signal output in the upper audio range. There is no clearly defined frequency limit at which tape output can be considered controlled solely by either factor. In Fig. 3-12 we see frequency response curves for a domestic tape, having a coercive force of about 300 oersteds, and for the German "L" tape, with a coercive force of about 90 oersteds. From these curves it is evident that a higher coercive force produces a better high-frequency response. But it is also true that the high-coer-

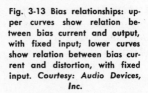

Fig. 3-13 Bias relationships: upper curves show relation between bias current and output, with fixed input; lower curves show relation between bias current and distortion, with fixed input. Courtesy: Audio Devices, Inc.

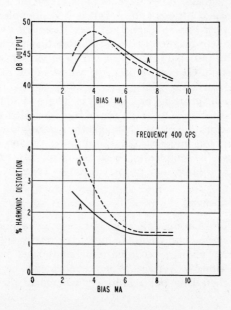

cive tapes produce a poorer low-frequency response. Therefore a compromise must be made between tapes with high remanence and those of highest coercive force.

The characteristics of today's first-line plastic tapes are reasonably similar, varying only moderately with different base materials and thicknesses. Performance quality depends primarily on the care devoted to achieving uniformity in both the magnetic coating and base materials.

The upper curves of Fig. 3-13 show (for two different modern tapes, *A* and *O*) the relationship between bias current and output for a fixed signal input of 400 cps. The two lower curves, in the same graph, show a reduction of distortion for an increase of bias for either tape. From this it is seen that output gains are derived for an increase of bias up to a certain operating point, beyond which the distortion levels off, while the output drops rapidly. We further see that a greater distortion content accompanies the greater output of tape *O*. Such differences are often chargeable to the use of different oxides in tapes.

Tape Life. Plastic tapes, such as the cellulose-acetate base, should not be exposed to continued temperatures above 80°F, nor should they be subjected to extended periods of high humidity. Excessive heat will cause brittleness, while dampness may cause adjacent layers to stick together. Tapes having historical value, which are to be stored for some years, should be kept in a humidifier with the temperature ranging between 60° and 70°F, and the humidity averaging between 40% and 60%. Even for temporary storage, important tapes should be kept in a cool location.

Magnetic tapes have both a magnetic and physical life term. Of the former little is known, but it is reasonable to assume that there will be a slow loss of magnetism over extended periods, as occurs with any permanent magnet. It is also possible that there may be greater depreciation for peak-amplitude levels than for lower levels, thereby introducing distortion. Cases have occurred where tapes, recorded at high levels and stored for some years (while being tightly reeled) showed effects of *magnetic printing* or *cross talk*. There is some cross talk evident between layers of any tape reeled and recorded at excessive levels (safety limitations against such magnetic printing are given later).

Several modern tapes minimize the problem of magnetic print-through by employing base materials of standard thickness together with a thinner-than-normal layer of specially-processed oxides.

Reproduction

For reproduction from a tape, the magnetic process of recording is reversed. The irregular and temporarily fixed orientation of coated particles upon a recorded tape establishes myriads of tiny magnetic fields along its surface. When a recorded tape travels past a reproducer head these tiny fields induce a voltage in the coils of the head. This voltage varies with the magnitude and polarity of the recorded signals and, when properly amplified, drives a loudspeaker to reproduce signals in correspondence with those originally recorded, thus the tape record is scanned magnetically.

Two major effects cause the response during playback to be far from *flat*. First, as will be explained, the reproducing-head output increases with frequency. Second, factors of self-demagnetization cause a rapid decline of frequency response above 5,000 cps. The voltage output from a reproducer is proportional to the *rate of change of the flux,* rather than to the amplitude of the flux. For a given distance along the tape, the rate of change of flux for a high frequency is greater than that for a low frequency; consequently, the voltage output of the reproducing head is proportional to frequency. This accounts for the 6-db-per-octave rise of the curve in Fig. 3-12.

The reproducing head is a generator having a stationary coil subjected to a changing magnetic field. Flux lines emanating from a recorded tape enter the reproducing-gap area and pass through the windings of the reproducing head, thereby inducing a voltage within the windings of the head.

Spurious Echoes. When a tape is recorded at excessive levels, spurious *magnetic printing* occurs from one layer to another after the recorded tape is wound on a reel. This condition may be avoided by confining the recording levels, by means of a limiter or other device, to peaks containing no more than 2% distortion at optimum bias. The higher the recorded level, the greater will be the spurious printing effects. These effects are sometimes called *echoes,* because they are heard as echoes when played back. High temperatures aggravate this crosstalk between layers of stored or reeled tape. Samples heated to 250°F have produced as many as four distinct echoes. As noted previously, this problem has been minimized in modern tapes by using base materials of standard thickness together with a thinner-than-normal layer of specially-processed oxides.

Frequency Response

The frequency response reproduced from a magnetic tape depends mainly upon the effective width of the reproducing gap, the speed of tape travel, and the magnetic characteristic of the entire system, including the tape itself.

Recording-gap width is of little consequence, but the recording-gap field current is important. Field intensity within the recording gap is almost directly proportional to the current in the recording-head coil. Current in the recording-head coil will be constant for most frequencies of the input signal, if a resistance is inserted in series with the coil which is large compared to the reactance of the coil. This series resistor should be considerably larger in value than the impedance of the recording head. The internal resistance of the driver amplifier is

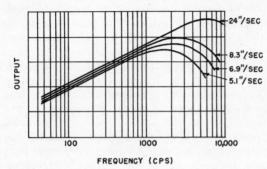

Fig. 3-14 Frequency response of oxide-coated paper tape at several recording speeds. Courtesy: Minn. Mining and Mfg. Co.

often used to serve this purpose; under this condition a constant input voltage should produce a constant intensity of the gap field for all frequencies. When a tried and proven optimum ratio between signal amplitude and bias amplitude is once set for a given tape, and the conditions stated above hold, the recorded signal should have low distortion and a high signal-to-noise ratio.

Reproducer output voltage is proportional to frequency and will rise at the rate of 6db per octave (Fig. 3-12) at the lower frequencies. It falls off at high frequencies because of demagnetization effects and the fixed width of the reproducing gap. Corrective equalization during reproduction will produce the overall response desired, and also result in a better signal-to-tape noise content (equalization is discussed later in this chapter).

Speed vs Frequency

Lower frequencies in the audio spectrum are practically independent of the speed at which the tape travels.

The low-frequency response, or the voltage output at any frequency for a given speed, however, is directly proportional to the remanent flux density (B_r) of the tape. The wavelengths at low frequencies are very long compared to air-gap length, hence the effect of demagnetization is negligible.

In the higher-frequency end of the spectrum the effect of self-demagnetization is very pronounced and increases rapidly as tape speed is reduced, as shown in Fig. 3-14. The high-frequency response is raised one octave when the tape speed is doubled. The high-frequency voltage is also proportional to the coercive force (H_c) of the tape.

Not long ago the better designed machines boasted of a frequency range of 1,000 cps per-inch second of tape speed. Advanced controls and more uniform dispersion of magnetic material in the present tapes have at least doubled that factor. The present relationship approximates 2,600 cps per inch second of tape speed; this figure holds presently for professional-type recordings. For special purposes the factor is easily expanded, but only at the expense of signal-to-noise content. Telemetering facilities, using wider than normal tape, have pushed the upper-frequency limit to the megacycle region. This is certainly proof of the constant promise from development laboratories. It guarantees the future of tape recording, which today is commercially available with an upper-frequency reproduction limit of 25 kc for high-quality sound systems.

Noise

Mechanical or magnetic sources of noise may mar otherwise clean recordings. Carelessness of mechanical construction may contribute to noise content. For example, either transverse or longitudinal vibrations of the tape during transport past the recording head will create some degree of background noise. Therefore, uniformity of pulling torque and tape transport is imperative for best results, and is an item which too often is ignored.

A lack of uniform smoothness of the recording tape can also cause output noise. If the magnetic coating is placed on a rough surface the overall output will be unnecessarily noisy.

Magnetic noise has a tendency to follow signal amplitude; this type of noise increases with the amplitude of the signal. It is caused by a disturbance of the magnetic particles as the tape becomes magnetized (that is, modulated). When the high-frequency bias control is properly adjusted, however, the content of this type of noise is sufficiently low to be masked by the signal, and therefore is not too objectionable. Theory suggests that magnetic noise originates on the sur-

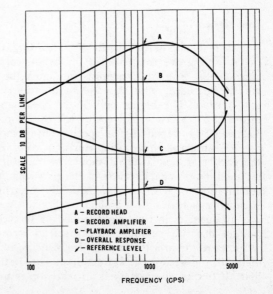

Fig. 3-15 Typical response curves with and without compensation. *Courtesy: Brush Development Co.*

A – RECORD HEAD
B – RECORD AMPLIFIER
C – PLAYBACK AMPLIFIER
D – OVERALL RESPONSE
✓ – REFERENCE LEVEL

SCALE 10 DB PER LINE

FREQUENCY (CPS)

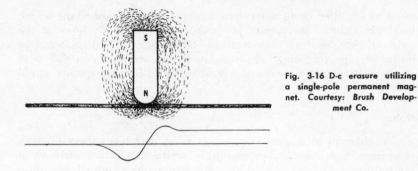

Fig. 3-16 D-c erasure utilizing a single-pole permanent magnet. *Courtesy: Brush Development Co.*

face of the tape, when the random elementary magnets which are smaller than the gap length become disturbed in their dormant orientation. This theory is borne out by the fact that in a saturated (d-c) tape the noise distribution has essentially the same frequency spread as it does in the demagnetized, a-c biased tape. The only difference is that there is a greater residual background noise in the saturated tape, which apparently is a function of the degree of saturation. Here again the high-frequency (a-c) biasing method of recording permits not only a better quality reproduction but also achieves noise reduction in the final recording.

Recording heads must be shielded against stray magnetic and electrostatic fields from nearby equipment to prevent foreign noises from being introduced into the record. Thermal noise and hum must also be held to a minimum through proper amplifier design.

Equalization

In magnetic as well as in disc recording, distortions occuring during recording are compensated for by *pre-emphasis* and *post-emphasis* equalization. Equalization must counteract the 6-db-per-octave rise previously discussed. The signal-to-noise ratio is also improved through equalization. The higher end of the spectrum may be augmented by means of a corrective network or left to droop, as in the curves of Fig. 3-12 and 3-14, depending on specific requirements.

Pre-emphasis equalization during a recording must be adjusted for the particular tape used; it should be variable, since it depends upon the modulation characteristic of the particular tape utilized. Adjustable equalization for both ends of the audio spectrum is advisable; however, equalizing facilities must be used with care. An excess boost of low register frequencies in the neighborhood of 40 cycles, for example, will introduce machine rumble. Since practical recording speeds for average purposes result in a loss of high frequencies, it is best to exaggerate the highs during recording. Pre-emphasis equalization can be adjusted so that all frequencies are likely to reach optimum levels before overload occurs. Post emphasis of *highs* (during playback) will increase the noise component in mid-frequency-range.

Compensating networks are usually inserted after the first amplifier stage. The initially low signal-input voltages should not be further reduced by the insertion of unnecessary losses prior to amplification. The same general principle applies to corrective networks used for post-emphasis compensation. Post-emphasis networks can be adjusted to complement pre-emphasis for overall flat reproduction.

Typical compensation curves are shown in Fig. 3-15; curve *A* shows the frequency response to be expected if flat amplifiers are used for both recording and reproducing with a composite of typical commercial tape recorders described in later chapters. Curve *B* in Fig. 3-15 shows the characteristic of the amplifier actually used for recording. Curve *C* shows the response of the playback amplifier, while curve *D* shows the overall frequency response resulting from superimposing curve *C* upon curves *A* and *B*. Actual equalization networks and their component values are detailed in Chapter 6.

Erasure (DC and AC)

It is merely necessary to apply a unidirectional magnetic field of sufficient magnitude to attain saturation in order to erase a magnetic recording from a tape. A single, strong permanent magnet applied to the tape as it moves past the pole piece, as shown in Fig. 3-16, will wipe out any previous recording. This method is not now used, however, since magnetic saturation of the tape produces a high content of ambient noise.

A better method of d-c erasure is shown in Fig. 3-17. Here two permanent magnets of opposite sign contact the tape during transit. Strong fields, first in one direction and then in the opposite, are applied to the tape. The resulting field alternation reduces the residual magnetism left over by the saturating field of the first pole. However, even when carefully adjusted, this method produces a somewhat higher content of residual tape noise than results from the use of high-frequency erasure.

Fig. 3-17 Erasure by two permanent magnets of opposite sign. The resultant alternation field reduces residual magnetism left by the single-pole type of erasure. *Courtesy: Brush Development Co.*

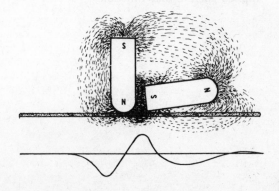

Fig. 3-18 Improved modern method of high-frequency erasure; the tape is demagnetized to a neutral condition. *Courtesy: Brush Development Co.*

High-Frequency Erasure. For the high-frequency method of erasure a signal of considerable magnitude from an ultrasonic power oscillator is applied to the windings of a laminated erasure head, which is similiar in construction to a ring-type recording head. This is the most popular erasing technique. Several requirements must be met, however, for proper operation. First, the erasure signal must be of greater magnitude than any signal it is required to erase; secondly, the erasure gap must be much wider (about 20 mils) than the recording-head gap. The erase-head gap literally spews its rapidly alternating flux into the tape, which is drawn across and in direct contact with it. Figure 3-18 illustrates the action which results in negligible remanence.

As the recorded tape nears the high-frequency field of the erasure gap, each magnetic particle on the tape surface becomes magnetized first in one direction and then in the other, due to the rapidly reversing field. As the particles cross the center of the gap they are saturated, the previous recording being completely erased. After the particles pass the gap center they are still subjected to alternating and fringing fluxes, which become rapidly weaker as the tape moves on. The result is that all residual magnetism is removed and the tape is left in a virgin or neutral state. A tape so erased has a very low noise component when used again. The erasure frequency is not critical. Often the same oscillator is used for both bias and erase, a weaker signal being applied for the bias function.

Chapter 4

MONAURAL AND BINAURAL RECORDERS

We now turn from the principles of how a magnetic signal is put on tape to a survey of the commercial instruments that make monaural and binaural recordings. Until a very few years ago all commercially available recorders were of the monaural or "monophonic" type, that is, the signals that they recorded were picked up by only one microphone. Such recordings provided no sensation concerning the direction and distance of individual sound sources. They provided sound, as it were, for only one ear.

It is now possible to record and reproduce the sensation of sound as it is heard with two ears. Two microphones are placed 6 to 8 inches apart to duplicate the directional sensitivity of the two human ears. The signals each picks up are simultaneously recorded on a "binaural recorder," producing two sound tracks side-by-side along the same length of tape. When these tracks are played back simultaneously through individual earphones, the result, called "binaural playback," gives the listener the sensation of being able to detect the direction and distance of the original sound sources. If the two tracks are played back through well separated loudspeakers, they produce a similar sensation known as "stereophonic sound."

Music recorded in this way has become so popular that a number of f-m stations now broadcast it frequently, and many f-m radio manufacturers produce equipment for reproducing the two sound channels from separate speakers. But binaural or stereo equipment is not restricted to recording and reproducing music alone. It is of significant use in a variety of educational and professional applications that will be considered in this section.

All tape recorders contain two major systems: the tape transport and the electronic. The tape transport system moves the tape past the magnetic heads at a constant speed for regular play; it also provides for rapid advance and rewind of the tape so that the listener may conveniently and quickly skip over or replay selected sections of the recording. The electronic system amplifies the audio-frequency signals supplied by a microphone, radio, television set, or record player and mixes them with high-frequency bias signals. The two combined signals are fed to the record head and then magnetically impressed upon the tape. In addition, the electronic system makes it possible to play back the magnetic signal on the tape by using a playback head to reconvert it to an electrical signal that is amplified and fed to a loudspeaker.

Monaural recorders meet the description in the previous paragraph. Binaural recorders have an identical tape transport but employ two complete electronic systems for simultaneously recording the two sound tracks side-by-side on the same tape. The erase, record, and playback heads are stacked one above the other to make it possible to record these parallel sound tracks.

This chapter begins with a review of the external features of monaural tape recorders and their controls, inputs, and outputs. It then reviews the methods utilized by monaural and binaural recorders for making multiple sound recordings on a single length of tape and discusses the outstanding features of binaural recorders. Finally, it surveys tape cartridges, accessory devices, and performance requirements. The internal features of the tape transport and electronics system, and their servicing, will be analyzed in chapters that follow.

EXTERNAL FEATURES

Basic Features of the Tape Transport

Figure 4-1 illustrates the basic features of the tape transport, which may be summarized as follows:

Supply Reel. The supply reel is a clear plastic spool for supplying the magnetic tape that is to be recorded upon or played back. This tape is moved past the magnetic heads and is wound up on the take up reel. The supply reel rests on a shaft projecting up from a small revolving

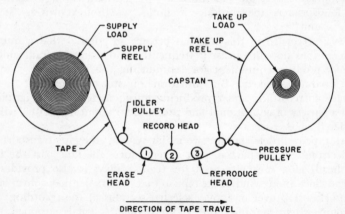

DIRECTION OF TAPE TRAVEL

Fig. 4-1 Basic tape-transport mechanism.

disc known as the "supply reel turntable." Slots in the reel's central hole key it to projections on the turntable, and the reel is turned or held at a stop by the turntable mechanism below the panel.

Standard supply reel diameters are shown in Table 4-1, together with the various lengths of tape that are stored and playing times at standard tape speeds. Reels in 5- and 7-inch diameters are readily available in clear red, yellow, green, and blue colors.

Recording Tape. Present-day recording tape is available in a variety of thicknesses and backing materials. The cheapest tape backing is made of acetate or other unspecified plastic; it is 1½ mils thick. The most durable tape backing of professional-quality is made of polyester film identified by DuPont's registered trademark "Mylar"; it is also 1½ mils thick.

Additional playing time can be obtained, without increase in reel size, by the use of thinner tape backing. Backing 1-mil thick provides 50% more playing time, and this tape is available in plastic or Mylar. Playing time can be doubled by the use of tape with a ½-mil backing, usually made of Mylar or "tempered" or "tensilized" Mylar, which is twice as strong as Mylar of the same thickness. Even thinner tape is available in "tempered" Mylar, and this has tripled the playing time of 1½-mil tape.

Table 4-1 lists standard tape thicknesses and their playing times for different reel diameters and tape speeds.

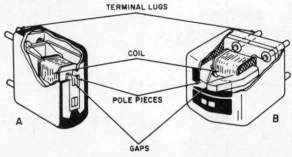

Fig. 4-2 Construction of typical erase (A) and record (B) heads. *Courtesy: Heath Co.*

Erase Head. Figure 4-2 shows the construction of a binaural erase head, comprising two erase heads stacked one above the other and molded in plastic into a single unit. The erase head is an electromagnet that is supplied with high-frequency alternating current. It has a laminated or nonlaminated C-shaped core with balanced windings, and the gap edges that touch the tape are precision ground and polished. The gap in the core of the erase head may be as wide as 0.008-inch and provides a diffused magnetic field that removes any previous magnetic signal on the tape without leaving a distinguishable signal of its own. Some erase heads have an E-shaped core that provides a double gap to produce an even more diffused magnetic field. A felt pad is usually employed to press the

TABLE 4-1

Standard Tape Thicknesses, Reel Sizes, and Playing Times at Various Speeds

Type of tape	Reel size, in.	Length, ft.	Standard tape speeds, ips		
			Total playing time*		
			1⅞	3¾	7½
Standard play, 1.5-mil acetate or Mylar	3	150	32 min	16 min	8 min
	5	600	2 hr 8 min	1 hr 4 min	32 min
	7	1200	4 hr 16 min	2 hr 8 min	1 hr 4 min
	10½	2400	8 hr 32 min	4 hr 16 min	2 hr 8 min
Long play, 1.0-mil acetate or Mylar	3	225	48 min	24 min	12 min
	5	900	3 hr 12 min	1 hr 36 min	48 min
	7	1800	6 hr 24 min	3 hr 12 min	1 hr 36 min
	10½	3600	12 hr 48 min	6 hr 24 min	3 hr 12 min
Extra long play, 0.5-mil Mylar tensilized	3	300	1 hr 4 min	32 min	16 min
	3¼	600	2 hr 8 min	1 hr 4 min	32 min
	5	1200	4 hr 16 min	2 hr 8 min	1 hr 4 min
	7	2400	8 hr 32 min	4 hr 16 min	2 hr 8 min
	10½	4800	17 hr 4 min	8 hr 32 min	4 hr 16 min

* The total time is for half-track monaural and for four-track stereo. To obtain the times for full-track recording and two-track stereo divide the times by 2. For 4-track monaural multiply the times by 2.

tape against the head to assure close and uniform contact.

The erase head operates only during the recording process and is not active during playback. Permanent-magnetic erase heads are sometimes used in modern portable recorders, primarily to reduce the number of electronic components and thereby achieve higher reliability. Some of these permanent-magnet erase heads contain a number of thin magnets laminated together so that the tape passes a succession of north-south pole combinations, thereby achieving an effect resembling alternating-current erasure.

Record Head. The construction of the record head (see Fig. 4-2) generally resembles that of the erase head, but laminated cores are almost always used. The gap is much smaller, ranging from 0.005-inch down to 0.00015-inch, to permit impressing high-frequency magnetic signals at moderate tape speeds. The function of the record head is to produce a sharply defined magnetic field having a magnitude proportional to the current in its windings. Since these currents are produced by the amplified audio input signal, the magnetic variations impressed upon the tape correspond to the frequency and amplitude variations in the original sound signal. This head operates only during the recording process.

Playback Head. The playback or "reproduce" head has essentially the same construction as the record head. When the magnetic variations on previously recorded tape pass the tap, they induce electrical currents within the winding. Since these voltage variations correspond to the frequency and amplitude of the magnetic variations on the tape, they can be amplified and fed to a loudspeaker to reproduce the original sound signal. The playback head is used only when playing back a recording.

Many recorders employ a single head that is employed both for playback and recording. These combination record/playback heads are switched so that they are connected as required to the record or playback electronic system.

Capstan. This is a rubber-rimmed shaft which is turned by an electric motor within the recorder cabinet. A freely turning pressure pulley presses the tape against the capstan, so that the turning of the capstan pulls the tape off the supply reel and past the magnetic heads at constant speed. In modern recorders used for music or voice recording, the highest speed at which the tape is pulled past the heads is 15 inches per second (ips). Recording speeds of 7½ and 3¾ ips are much more common for music *and* voice, whereas speeds of 1⅞ and 15/16 ips are most common for voice only. Many recorders have provisions for driving the tape at a selection of two or more of these speeds.

The use of a capstan to drive the tape assures a more nearly constant tape speed than can be practically achieved by driving the reels only. The reason for this is that a single turn of a full supply reel delivers much more tape when the reel is full (7-inch diameter) than when the reel is empty (2-inch diameter). The same is true of the length of tape wound up by a single turn of the supply reel. Thus, to achieve a constant tape speed by means of reel drive alone would require a continuously variable speed drive that would be much more complex than the capstan method.

Take-up Reel. This reel is identical to and interchangeable with the supply reel and is mounted on a turntable in the same manner. Its function is to receive and store the tape coming from the capstan.

Tape-Guides. Slotted posts and brackets are employed to assure that the tape travels in a straight line from the supply reel, past the magnetic heads and onto the take-up reel. Without these tape guides, the tape could move up or down out of a line with the gaps in the magnetic heads. Such motion would also make the tape slip above or below the take-up reel, thereby spilling or becoming entangled.

Tension Devices. Some recorders employ tape guides or freely turning pulleys known as idlers; these are mounted on arms to which spring tension is applied. When the tape passes over them, they act to keep an extended length of it under uniform moderate tension. When sudden speed changes take place, extra tape can be supplied to prevent breakage and extra tape can be taken up to prevent spilling. The uniform tension that is maintained also assists in maintaining constant tape speed during recording and playback.

Standard Controls and Indicators

Figure 4-3 shows a monaural tape recorder having controls and indicators that are common to most recorders, although the details and general layout vary considerably among different manufacturers. The purpose and basic variations of these controls are reviewed in the paragraphs that follow.

Function Selector. The function selector has vital and extensive electrical, mechanical, and electronic control functions. This control usually takes the form of a row of push bars or buttons, although it also appears in the form of a "joystick" or rotary selector. Both mechan-

Fig. 4-3 Sony Model TC-802 portable tape recorder. Controls and indicators are located on forward strip and are identified left to right: reset for digital tape counter, digital tape counter, record level meter, speed selector switch, volume control, function selector keys. *Courtesy: Sony Corp.*

ical linkages and electrical switches are actuated by the function selector to place the recorder in its five basic modes of operation: the (1) stop, (2) record, (3) playback, (4) fast-forward, and (5) fast-rewind modes.

When the stop mode is selected, both reels are braked. Heads and pressure pads are separated, as well as the capstan and its pressure roller. This provides a clear path for the tape between all contact areas and facilitates tape loading and unloading. It is almost a universal recorder rule that the selector be set to stop when the recorder is not being used or when one setting is being changed to the other.

In both the record or playback modes, the tape is pressed against the heads. The pressure roller presses the tape against the capstan, which then pulls the tape past the heads at constant speed. The discharged tape is wound up on the take-up reel. Mechanical functions are identical in both these modes, the difference being in the switching of the heads and the internal electronics.

The fast-forward and fast-rewind modes of operation are provided to permit a means for rapidly shuttling the tape back and forth so that entire sections can be skipped over or replayed as desired. In both these modes, the pressure roller and capstan are separated, and the tape is moved by the turning of the reels.

Speed Selector. Many tape recorders have a knob or lever for selecting one of two or more speeds at which the tape will be driven during recording or playback. As indicated earlier, the standard speeds used in tape recorders include 15, $7\frac{1}{2}$, $3\frac{3}{4}$, $1\frac{7}{8}$ and 15/16 ips — the higher speeds being used for music and the lower for voice. Tape recorders differ in that some require the speed selection to be made with the function selector set at stop and others with this selector set at record or play.

Tape Counter. Most tape recorders have some type of dial or counter arrangement connected to the tape transport mechanism to make it convenient to locate specific passages on the tape. The number indicated on the counter is proportional to the number of turns of the reel to which the counter is connected (either the take-up or supply reel). It does not give directly the number of feet of tape used, since each turn of the reel will not contain the same length of tape. For example, assume that the counter is connected to the take-up reel. As the take-up reel takes on more tape, each turn will contain more tape. To make use of the counter, merely set it at zero at the beginning of the tape and keep a written record of the counter reading at significant points on the tape. Graduations are often quite fine; they sometimes permit locating a specific point on the tape with an error of less than a few inches.

Tone and Volume Controls. In common with radios, television sets, and record players, tape recorders have knobs for controlling volume and tone. The on-off switch is normally associated with one of these knobs. The volume control usually has a dual purpose: (1) adjusting the volume of the sound coming out of the loudspeaker during playback, and (2) adjusting the amplitude of the record head magnetic signal during recording.

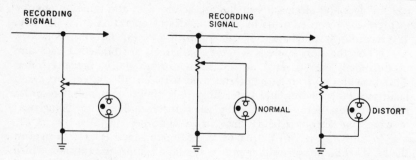

Fig. 4-4 Basic arrangement for using one and two neon bulbs for record level indication.

Record-Level Indicator. It has been indicated in previous chapters that there is an ideal level for the signal being recorded on the tape. A higher recording level results in distortion, a lower level in increased noise. The record-level indicator is a convenient device for viewing and adjusting the signal level while the recording is being made. While a recording is being made, the volume control is set so that a signal of maximum expected loudness causes the indicator to show maximum permissible distortion.

Three types of record-level indicators are in widespread use: the neon lamp, the magic-eye tube, and the VU meter. Each has its advantages and disadvantages.

The neon-tube indicator is the simplest and cheapest type. In its most basic form, the circuit consists of a neon tube connected across a voltage divider, as shown in Fig. 4-4. When a single neon tube is used, the (internal) potentiometer is set so that the lamp lights when the signal is at a level producing maximum permissible distortion. The operator adjusts the panel volume control so that the lamp lights almost continuously during the loudest passages. At such a setting, the lamp will blink occasionally during passages of average loudness. Although this method of adjustment may seem imprecise, its extreme simplicity makes it quite satisfactory to all but high-fidelity enthusiasts.

A more precise arrangement is provided by recorders containing two neon lamps. One lamp (usually marked *distort*) has its potentiometer adjusted so that it lights when the signal level reaches the point of maximum permissible distortion. The other lamp (usually marked *normal*) has its potentiometer adjusted so that it lights at a signal level 5 to 10 db below that of the *distort* lamp. At this level it blinks almost continuously during passages of normal loudness and assures the user that everything is going well.

The magic-eye indicator (Fig. 4-5) is connected to the recording amplifier in the same manner as the single neon tube. The potentiometer is adjusted so that the shadow area closes down to a very fine wedge with no overlap when the signal is at the level producing maximum permissible distortion. At such a setting, average signals half close the eye, and signals at too low a level do not close the eye at all. With an indi-

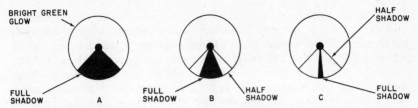

Fig. 4-5 Appearance of "magic-eye" record level indicator under various recording conditions: (A) No signal; (B) normal signal level; (C) peak signal level.

cator of this type it is easy to adjust the recording level during average or low passages and to be well prepared for loud passages.

The VU meter (Fig. 4-6) is found on many machines intended for high-fidelity enthusiasts and for professional use. The term "VU" means volume units, which are normally calibrated in decibels above and below zero on the meter scale. In use, the volume control is set so that the pointer is at the zero indication on the scale during a passage of maximum loudness. This zero indication marks the level of maximum permissible distortion. VU meters also have a percentage scale in which the 100% level corresponds to the zero db level; some users find this scale more satisfactory. Recordings of average sound level are made with the pointer varying between − 5 and − 10 db, which corresponds roughly to between 30 and 55 on the percentage scale.

In some recorders the VU meter can be switched to measure, and permit adjustment of, bias and erase current and the level of the signal in the playback amplifier. Although the VU meter adds to the functions

Fig. 4-6 VU meter record level indicator as used on Ampex Model 602 tape recorder. Courtesy: Ampex Corp.

that can be monitored and adjusted, it requires more comprehension and experience in its proper use than other indicators. Neon-tube and magic-eye indicators react instantly in response to sudden changes in signal level, but the VU meter movement has mechanical inertia and can lag almost a half-second behind sudden, sustained rises in level. Signal amplitude changes that last only a fraction of a second result in a needle reaction that is lower than it should be, and there may be no reaction at all. Consequently, the tape recorder user must be familiar with the type of material that he is recording and must gain experience with the recording levels that are most suitable for use with different materials. If these requirements are observed, the VU meter is the most precise of all record-level indicators.

Monitor Switch. Most tape recorder users like to listen to a recording as it is being made, so that they can assure themselves that all is going well and so that they can omit or adjust the volume of certain passages to suit their individual tastes. Tape recorders often have a monitor switch that permits the signal to be heard from the tape recorder's own loudspeaker or through supplementary earphones.

When the recorder has a separate playback head, the signal that is heard is an almost immediate playback of the signal that is being impressed upon the tape by the record head, and the effectiveness of the recording process is immediately proven. Such recorders often have what is known as "A-B switching." This is a monitor switch that permits the recordist to hear either the incoming signal being fed to the record head or the played-back version of that same signal. By frequently comparing the second with the first, the recordist can easily determine if his adjustments are producing the desired result.

When the instrument has a combination record/playback head, the signal that is heard is the one being applied to the recording head. Hearing this signal does not prove that a good recording is being made.

Inputs and Outputs

In its most basic form, a tape recorder has a wired-in microphone and a built-in loudspeaker. It is then capable only of making recordings through its microphone and playing them back through its loudspeaker. Only a few machines, however, such as office dictation machines and ultra-compact portable units, are so restricted. Most tape recorders intended for home and general portable use have a number of inputs and outputs available.

Many recorders have at least two inputs. One of these is for feeding in signals from radios, television sets, record players, other tape recorders, and high-signal-level microphones. This input is usually marked "radio-phono-high level microphone" and is useful for most recorder applications. The second input is for low-impedance, low-signal-level microphones, such as the dynamic and ribbon microphones considered later in this chapter under "Accessories." This second input feeds into a special preamplifier that provides the necessary impedance match and added gain required. The output of this preamplifier is connected to the same point in the recording amplifier as the input point previously mentioned.

A few tape recorders have additional inputs for high-level or low-level signals. These are intended to permit mixing together simultaneous signals from several sources such as a radio and a microphone, a record player and a tape recorder, etc. It is often desirable to be able to control the relative levels of these different signals so that some will be predominant and others subdued. Sometimes this must be accomplished by controlling the signal level at its original source, but at other times the tape recorder may have individual volume controls for adjusting the levels of one or more of these signals.

Since most tape recorders are designed to be reasonably compact, they cannot contain a loudspeaker and baffle system that would be satisfactory to high-fidelity enthusiasts, even though they may contain excellent power amplifiers. Consequently, many tape recorders contain one, two, or more output connectors for feeding the output of its amplifiers to auxiliary high-fidelity speakers. Frequently, these connectors are so constructed that when they are used, the tape recorder's own speakers are disconnected.

Because high-fidelity enthusiasts may have unusually high standards for power amplifiers, some tape recorders have an "external amplifier" output connector. Use of this connector usually switches the signal away from the tape recorder's own power amplifier and into the external amplifier and speaker system provided by the user.

Most tape recorders have a so-called "public address" mode of operation. In this mode, the tape transport is set to stop, but the electronics system is not turned off. Under these conditions, any radio/phono or microphone input signal is connected through the play-back amplifier to the loudspeaker. Thus, the instrument can be used as a public address system or as a high-quality amplifier for a record player or radio.

BINAURAL RECORDERS

Comparison of Monaural and Binaural Recording

Recording Two Monaural Sound Tracks. The original tape machines recorded only a single sound track on a length of tape. Because each magnetic variation extended across almost the full width of the tape, high signal levels were generated in the play-back and good signal-to-noise ratios resulted. With improvements in the tape, the magnetic heads, and the electronics, it was found that very satisfactory signal-to-noise ratios could be obtained if the sound track occupied only slightly less than half the tape. Now it became possible to double the playing time provided by a single reel of tape.

This procedure, illustrated by Fig. 4-7, is now employed in nearly all monaural recorders. First, sound track is recorded on one side of

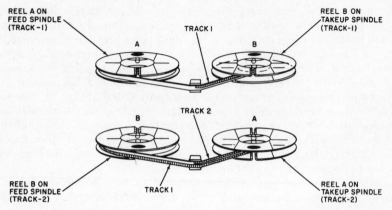

Fig. 4-7 How monaural sound can be recorded on adjacent sound tracks. Courtesy: Sony Corp.

the tape. When the end is reached, the supply and take-up reels are interchanged and turned over. Then, without further adjustment, the sound can continue to be recorded in an adjacent track on the tape. Thus the playing time provided by a single reel of tape can be doubled.

Recording Binaural Sound Tracks. The capability to record two sound tracks on a single tape makes it possible to produce binaural recorders. Machines of this type contain a single tape transport with two complete electronic channels. The magnetic heads of these two electronic systems are stacked one above the other, and the binaural recording process takes place as illustrated in Fig. 4-8. A machine that makes recordings of this type is known as a "two-track stereo recorder" or a "two-track, two-channel recorder."

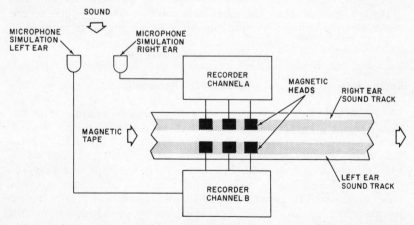

Fig. 4-8 Recording two sound tracks simultaneously to produce a binaural or stereophonic recording.

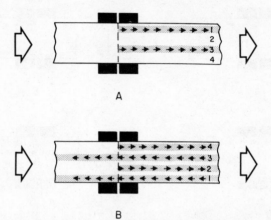

Fig. 4-9 Technique for making four-track stereo recordings: (A) The two stereo channels are recorded on nonadjacent tracks in one direction (tracks 1 and 3) from one end of reel to other; (B) at end of reel, tape is turned over and recorded on alternate tracks (tracks 2 and 4). Split black bars on each side of tape symbolize location of recording gap.
Courtesy: Ampex Corp.

Although this method of making binaural recordings produces a highly desirable result, it does not permit doubling the playing time as is possible with monaural recordings. Much effort was thus expended in perfecting magnetic heads and electronic systems, and it became possible to record four good-quality sound tracks on a single width of tape. The process is illustrated in Fig. 4-9. A machine of this type is known as a "four-track stereo recorder" or a "four-track, two-channel recorder."

Four-Track Monaural Recording. The capability of making four sound tracks on a single reel of tape quadruples the playing time of monaural recordings. This can be accomplished easily with four-track, two-channel machines if the user is willing to restrict himself to monaural recording. The procedure is illustrated in Fig. 4-10. It is possible that single-channel machines will be developed to permit making four-track monaural recordings, but the advantage obtained may well be cancelled by the complexities of raising and lowering the single-channel magnetic heads to accomplish this.

Two Channel Recorders

Two-channel recorders have a single tape transport and two complete and identical electronic recording and playback channels. Thus a recorder of this type (Fig. 4-11) has two volume controls, two tone controls, two record level indicators, two sets of inputs, and two sets of outputs.

Because producing stereophonic sound requires that the speakers be separated by a distance of at least 6 feet, it is impractical to mount both speakers in the same recorder cabinet. Different manufacturers have

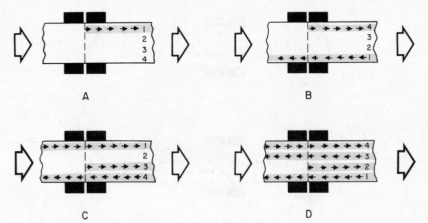

A

B

C

D

Fig. 4-10 Technique of using two-channel, four-track recorder for making four-track monophonic recording: (A) Tape is recorded on one-fourth its width (Mono 1 position); (B) at end of reel, tape is turned over, and second track is recorded in opposite direction (Mono 1 position); (C) at end of second track, tape is turned over again, and third track is recorded in same direction of original recording (Mono 2 position); (D) reel is turned over again, and final track is recorded (Mono 2 position). Mono positions refer to the two different sound recording channels. Courtesy: Ampex Corp.

provided different solutions to this problem. Some supply two speakers that are attached to the main case for easy carrying but can be detached and connected by cables to the recorder unit when in use. Other manufacturers mount one speaker in the recorder case and the second speaker in a detachable lid. Still other manufacturers supply only one power supply and loudspeaker. The playback channel for the second head has only a preamplifier, and the user can employ a separate hi-fi amplifier and loudspeaker system to complete the second channel. Various combi-

Fig. 4-11 Sony Model 500 illustrates how a two-channel recorder employs only a single tape transport but has two complete electronic channels. Courtesy: Sony Corp.

nations of these solutions are also obtainable in commercial two-channel recorders.

Stereophonic recordings are made in the same manner as monaural recordings, except that consideration must be given to the fact that two almost identical recordings must be made simultaneously. The problem is simplest when recording a stereophonic broadcast over an f-m radio equipped with stereo outputs. In this situation the two sound signals have already been transformed into electrical signals of equal frequency response and volume level. The tape recorder operator has only to record both signals with equal readings on the recording level indicator, although he should occasionally monitor both signals to assure himself that they are being recorded at equal levels.

When an original recording is being made with two microphones, it is important that the microphones have identical frequency response and signal level characteristics. Although minor differences can be corrected with the recorder's volume and tone controls, large differences in microphone characteristics may produce enough difference in the tonal quality of the two played-back sound tracks to mask the desired stereophonic effect. The placement of the two microphones can be very much a matter of individual preference. Moderately directional microphones can be placed 6 to 10 inches apart and directed from 45 to 90 degrees away from each other towards different sides of a large sound source. The sense of depth and direction can be exaggerated, sometimes with very desirable results, by a much larger separation between the two microphones.

Special Applications of Two-Channel Recorders

Note that binaural or stereo recorders have often been identified by the term "two-channel" recorders. This is because they are not restricted to stereophonic recording, and their other applications, which are extensive may be considered to be even more important.

Instead of recording two almost identical sound tracks on the tape, as in stereo recording, one can record sound tracks that are completely different, although related. For example, a language teacher can record a lesson through Channel A of a tape recorder, and this lesson can include pronunciation exercises, questions and answers, with appropriate pauses. Then a student can listen to the teacher's lesson on Channel A, while recording his responses on Channel B. Depending upon the method of teaching that is being used, the teacher may later listen to the student's answers on Channel B, or the student can simultaneously listen to both the teacher's lesson and his own responses. The student can then repeat the process of rerecording his answers until he is satisfied that he has mastered the goal of the lesson. The Channel B recording can then be erased, and the same lesson on Channel A can be used by another student.

This teaching technique is useful in a wide variety of basic and ad-

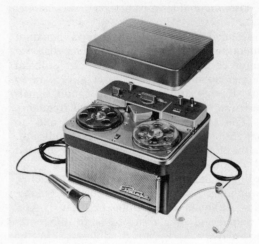

Fig. 4-12 Ekotape Model 510-1 Portable Tape Teaching Laboratory. *Courtesy: Webster Electric Co.*

vanced subjects and is beginning to be used quite extensively by many educational systems throughout the country. Some tape recorder manufacturers are beginning to specialize in the production of student recorders, sound study booths, and teacher master control consoles. Examples are shown in Figs. 4-12 and 4-13.

The same techniques can be used by actors, singers, musicians, and all those who perform with voice or instrument in conjunction with others. For example, an actor can have a recording made during a rehearsal or performance of a play in which he will appear. The recording is made on Channel A and the part of interest is dropped out by the simple expediency of turning down the volume control or switching off the microphone while it is being spoken. Then the actor can listen to

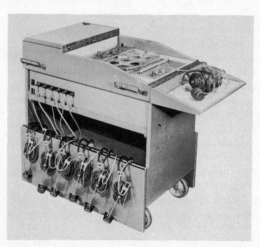

Fig. 4-13 Ekotape Model WTLM Mobile Tape Teaching Laboratory. *Courtesy: Webster Electric Co.*

Channel A, while recording his part on Channel B. He can then listen to both channels simultaneously and judge for himself the effectiveness of his performance and the corrections required. The process can be repeated as often as necessary until the part is mastered. This procedure can be used by all vocal or instrumental performers, but it should be noted that the final "polish" to any performance requires the guidance of the director or conductor.

A variety of novelty recordings, both professional and amateur, can be made with a two-channel recorder in the "sound-on-sound" mode of operation. This technique is most easily explained by means of an example. A singer accompanying himself on a guitar records a song into Channel A. He then connects the output of Channel A to the input of Channel B and also connects the microphone to an alternate input of Channel B. Then while listening to himself being recorded on Channel B, he sings the same song into the microphone, but he plays and sings a slightly different variation of the same song. When Channel B is played back it will sound like two voices and two instruments accompanying each other on the same sound track. Then the process can be repeated by recording Channel B plus a third voice and instrument into Channel.

TAPE CARTRIDGES

Some manufacturers are of the opinion that they can widely popularize their tape recorders if they can eliminate the problems of loading the tape onto the machine. Closely associated with this is the problem of extending the period of play-back time with minimum attention on the part of the user. The basic solution to these two problems has been the development and production of a tape cartridge and a recorder that provides maximum convenience when used with this cartridge. Although a number of cartridges have been developed for this purpose, the somewhat different solutions of the Radio Corporation of America and Viking of Minneapolis appear to be most representative.

RCA Tape Cartridge

The RCA Tape cartridge is illustrated in Fig. 4-14. It contains a supply and take-up reel mounted in a compact plastic holder equipped with end-of-reel shutoff devices, tape guides, and erase-preventing interlocks. The capstan, the record/play-back head, and the erase head engage the tape through the openings shown along the edge near the straight portion of the tape. Two knockouts along the opposite edge of the holder permit the tape to be erased and rerecorded as long as they are in place. When a desirable tape is recorded, the knockouts are removed to permit the operation of interlocks that prevent accidental erasure. The openings must be sealed with adhesive tape if it is desired to rerecord the tape. Prerecorded tapes are sold in cartridges with these knockouts removed.

The RCA tape cartridge measures $7\frac{1}{4} \times 5 \times \frac{1}{2}$ inch and holds

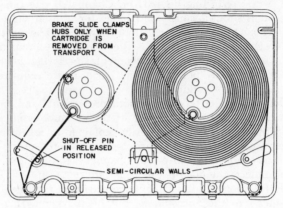

BRAKE SLIDE CLAMPS
HUBS ONLY WHEN
CARTRIDGE IS
REMOVED FROM
TRANSPORT

SHUT-OFF PIN
IN RELEASED
POSITION

SEMI-CIRCULAR WALLS

Fig. 4-14 Outstanding construction features of RCA tape cartridge. *Courtesy: RCA Sales Corp.*

600 feet of quarter-inch tape 1-mil thick. Recorders made for use with this cartridge employ four sound tracks. At $3\frac{3}{4}$-ips tape speed, a 1-hour stereo recording can be made by turning over the cartridge at the end of the first run. Playing time can be doubled by operation at $1\frac{7}{8}$ ips. Both of the stated times can be doubled when making 4-track monaural recordings.

Viking Tape Cartridge

Viking of Minneapolis employs a somewhat different concept in their tape cartridge. This cartridge plays a continuous loop of tape wound on a single hub as shown in Fig. 4-15. As the hub turns clockwise, the capstan pulls tape out from the center of the reel, and the turning of the reel takes up this tape onto the outside of the reel. To keep the tape moving at constant speed, many turns must be taken off the inside of the reel for each turn of the outside. This is assisted by the turning of the reel and the use of lubricated tape, both of which permit the various layers of tape to slide easily over one another.

The Viking tape cartridge is extremely compact in that almost the entire area inside is occupied by tape. Tape guides and openings in one edge of the cartridge permit easy engagement of the heads and capstan. The machines made for use with this cartridge offer a variety of head configurations including one, two, and four tracks with monaural or stereo and automatic stop capabilities. These sizes of cartridges are available, permitting playing times at $7\frac{1}{2}$ ips as short as 4.8 seconds and as long as 45 minutes per track. These playing times can be doubled by playing at $3\frac{3}{4}$ ips, and doubled again by using tape with magnetic coating on both sides and twisted to form a moebius loop. Loading devices are available to make it convenient to load specially desired lengths of tape into the cartridge.

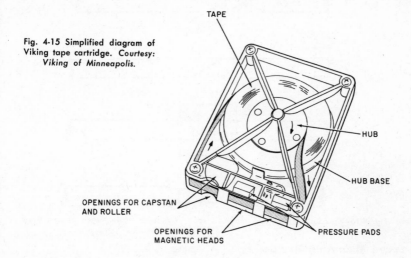

Fig. 4-15 Simplified diagram of Viking tape cartridge. Courtesy: Viking of Minneapolis.

TAPE

HUB

HUB BASE

OPENINGS FOR CAPSTAN AND ROLLER

OPENINGS FOR MAGNETIC HEADS

PRESSURE PADS

ACCESSORIES

Since tape recorder manufacturers have designed their products to take care of all ordinary operating conditions, there are very few accessory devices available or required. The most common accessories include tape splicing devices, speed measuring devices, head demagnetizers, bulk tape erasers, tape cleaning and lubricating devices, mixers, microphones, power amplifiers, and loudspeakers.

Tape Splicers

Modern recording tape is quite strong, and modern tape recorders handle it sufficiently gently to avoid any breaks during normal operation. The rare breaks that occur and the occasional sections that one may desire to cut out require no accessories other than a pair of scissors and a roll of splicing tape intended for this use. The splice is made by cutting and trimming the tape as shown in Fig. 4-16. One should use only splicing material that has been specially made for magnetic tape; the adhesive used in conventional plastic tape spreads out from under the cut edges and gums the capstan and the heads.

If extensive tape editing is to be done, a tape splicing device may be convenient. These devices clamp the tape in place while the cutting and splicing is performed. Prices range from about $1.00 for a simple plastic block with clamps that hold the tape while cutting is performed with a razor blade, to over $50 for a machine that does the job quickly and automatically.

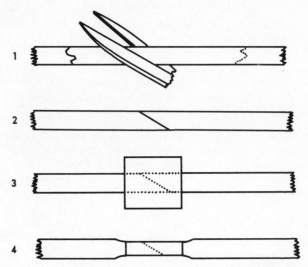

Fig. 4-16 Procedure for splicing magnetic tape. *Courtesy: Westinghouse Electric Corp.*

Speed Measuring Devices

A variety of stroboscopic discs are available for measuring tape speed. These devices help the user only by indicating when servicing is necessary. They are, however, very useful to the service man who must make the required adjustments. Operating principles of these devices, and the techniques for using them, are described in the Maintenance Section of Chapter 7.

Demagnetizers and Bulk Erasers

With extensive use magnetic heads become permanently magnetized. This adds noise to the tape and causes loss in high frequency response. Head demagnetizers such as those shown in Fig. 4-17 should be employed after every 10 to 20 hours of recorder use to prevent these effects. An explanation of the difficulties caused by the magnetization of heads and the techniques for demagnetizing them are included in the Maintenance Section of Chapter 7.

When high-quality ultra-low-noise recordings are to be made, the erase head cannot be relied upon to remove completely all previous sig-

Fig. 4-17 Head demagnetizer. *Courtesy: Audio Devices, Inc.*

Fig. 4-18 Magneraser Senior, a bulk eraser for use with all sizes of tape reels. Courtesy: Amplifier Corporation of America.

nals that might appear as noise. A bulk eraser, such as the one shown in Fig. 4-18, is usually an a-c solenoid that generates a powerful 60-cycle magnetic field. This field completely erases all previous signals in several seconds. Depending upon the type, the tape reel is slowly revolved over the eraser and then slowly removed to a distance, or the eraser is slowly moved over the tape reel and then slowly removed. The powerful "scrambling" action of the magnetic particles on the tape leaves them in a completely random pattern. Never bring the bulk eraser near the recorder, where its strong field can magnetize heads or damage VU meters.

Tape and Head Cleaners

A variety of devices are available for cleaning magnetic tape and heads. Tape cleaning and lubricating devices usually consist of a felt block, plastic sponge, or cloth impregnated with a silicone lubricant. These devices wipe off any dust and lightly lubricate the tape to prevent head wear. The only precaution to observe with these devices is to make sure that only a very light coating of lubricant is applied. Excessive lubricant can spread to the capstan and pressure roller surface where it can cause periodic slipping, with resultant wow.

Cleaning the magnetic heads is an important part of maintenance if optimum performance is to be maintained at all times. The importance of head cleaning and the techniques and materials for accomplishing it are described in detail in the Maintenance section of Chapter 7. Tape recorder users should be encouraged to clean magnetic heads periodically by means of these techniques. If they hesitate to undertake such procedures, they can employ a device known as the "WalscoKleen-Tape" which is a 100-foot length of ¼-inch wide absorbent material impregnated with cleaning materials and wound on a tape reel. The material is run through the recorder exactly as if it were magnetic tape, and it cleans and polishes the magnetic heads.

Mixers

When two or more microphones are connected to the same tape recorder input, their various signal levels must be adjusted to produce the desired effect. This is accomplished by a mixer unit of either the passive or active type.

A passive mixer consists of a number of potentiometers. Each microphone is connected across a potentiometer, and the sliding contacts of all the potentiometers are connected together and to the tape recorder input. By adjusting the settings of the various potentiometers, the various signal amplitudes can be adjusted to produce the desired balance among them. The disadvantage of mixers of this type is that every potentiometer adjustment changes the leading on the others and thus affects all signal levels to some degree.

Active mixers contain an amplifier stage for each microphone. Each microphone output is connected to the input of an amplifier through a potentiometer, and all the amplifier outputs are connected together to the tape recorder input. Thus the amplifier stages isolate the level controls from each other, and interaction is minimized.

Passive and active mixers for two, three, four, or more microphones are available from various tape recorder and electronic equipment manufacturers.

Microphones

Most home and educational recorders are supplied with microphones that are adequate for such use. However, most such recorders, and all serious hi-fidelity and professional units, have provisions for connecting optional high quality units.

The economy- and averaged-priced recorder is normally supplied with a piezoelectric microphone with a crystal or ceramic element. In a unit of this type the pressure of the sound waves is applied to a diaphragm and transmitted to the pressure-sensitive element. The result is a voltage that varies in frequency and amplitude, corresponding to the variations in the sound waves. Low-cost crystal microphones have an approximately flat response between 50 and 7,000 cps. More expensive crystal units have responses that are comparable with responses of other types of microphones. Crystal microphones are easily damaged by moisture and extreme temperatures, but piezoelectric units with ceramic elements have even better characteristics and are much less easily damaged by extreme temperatures and humidity. These microphones have impedances of several million ohms and require the tape recorder to have an input impedance in the same order of magnitude.

Dynamic microphones produce an output voltage by using a diaphragm to vibrate a coil in the presence of a permanent magnetic field. High-quality units of this type have a reasonably flat frequency response from 50 to 15,000 cps. Ribbon microphones employ the same principles; the sound waves vibrate a thin metal ribbon between the poles of a permanent magnet. Capacitor microphones contain two plates across which several hundred volts of direct current are applied through a resistor. Sound waves vibrate one of the plates, and the changes in capacitance produce a signal voltage across the resistor. This voltage is applied to the grid of a miniature amplifier tube in the microphone. These three types of microphones have excellent frequency response, but high-quality units may cost as much as several hundred dollars.

Piezoelectric microphones have impedances of several million ohms and require the tape recorder to have an input impedance in the same order of magnitude. Capacitor microphones are also high-impedance units, but the amplifier tube located inside lowers the impedance, and a built-in transformer provides additional step-down. Both dynamic and ribbon microphones are low-impedance devices and produce large signal currents at low voltage. For signal transmission through cable lengths in the order of 10 feet, a transformer is used to raise the impedance to the order of 25,000 ohms and also raise the signal level. This signal can be connected directly to the tape recorder input. For signal transmission through cables from 10 to 200 feet long, the transformer raises the impedance to a range between 30 and 600 ohms, and a transformer is used at the tape recorder input to raise the impedance to the order of 25,000 ohms.

Performance Standards

The performance of a tape recorder may be limited either by its mechanical or electronic characteristics or by a combination of both. Given the best possible tape transport, a recorder may still be incapable of top performance because of inadequate electronic equipment.

Frequency response characteristics are a major consideration in determining the cost of an installation. In general, the wider the frequency response, the greater the cost. The following table lists the minimum frequency characteristics suggested for various applications. In each case the electrical response is down 5 db at the limits given:

RECOMMENDED FREQUENCY RANGE MINIMA

(Courtesy: Audio Devices, Inc., Manufacturers of Audiotape)

For home use, for speech only:	100 to 4,000 cps
For home use, primarily for music:	70 to 7,500 cps
For home use, for one seriously interested in good music:	40 to 12,000 cps
For schools, for motivation in elementary schools:	100 to 5,000 cps
For schools, for English, drama, and history classes, where it is somewhat desirable to reveal poor speech:	70 to 7,500 cps

For schools, for speech and music classes, where
   subtle faults must be clearly revealed, and
   fine music pleasingly presented: 40 to 12,000 cps
For broadcasting, speech only: 70 to 7,500 cps
For broadcasting music: 40 to 15,000 cps

The last two items have been established by the National Association of Broadcasters (NAB), formerly the National Association of Radio
and Television Broadcasters (NARTB) as their *minimum* standards
for portable equipment and for professional studio installations.

In a home recorder the signal-to-noise ratio should be better than
35 db and can be expected to be as high as 50 db. In professional instruments the signal-to-noise ratio should be in the range of 45 to 60 db,
whereas in laboratory recorders the ratio may be as high as 70 db.

Wow and flutter for sound recorders is normally measured by a
flutter meter calibrated in percentages on an rms or average basis. A
percentage of 0.5 on these bases should be considered very poor, whereas
0.25% should be considered good for home use and fair for professional
applications. A value of 0.05% is typical of a very good professional
recorder.

Harmonic distortion for professional equipment should be less than
2% at peak output whereas 5% is adequate for most applications. Intermodulation noise for simultaneous signals at 60 and 7,000 cps should
be less than 8% if high fidelity music recordings are to be made and
played back.

Chapter 5

TAPE TRANSPORT MECHANISMS

The previous chapter has described the basic components of tape recorders and has indicated common standards of operation. Thus far it has been shown that the function of the tape transport is to move the tape past the heads at constant standardized speeds during recording and playback and at high speed during rapid wind and rewind. The ostensibly simple process of unwinding a roll of tape from one reel, drawing it past the magnetic heads, and then winding it onto another reel is, in fact, not at all simple. Present achievements realized in tape recorders are a tribute to design engineers.

The vast majority of tape recorders manufactured today employ a single motor to drive the capstan and tape reels in the standard operational modes of record, playback, fast forward, and rewind. Such recorders include the full range from professional units of highest quality and fidelity, through moderate-priced home recorders, and on to instruments employing a minimum of components to achieve either maximum economy or portability. Recorders of this type employ surprisingly varied arrangements of pulleys, belts, clutches, brakes, and mechanical linkages to provide the standard operational modes and record/playback at a selection of speeds.

Recorders employing two and three motors have been much more popular in previous years. Use of multiple motors in a tape transport greatly simplifies many of the mechanical problems involved; such use also increases weight, sometimes increases cost, and adds to the problems of electro-magnetic shielding to reduce electrical noise to a minimum.

Quality cannot be evaluated on the basis of the *type* of tape transport that is used. Good engineering and rigid quality control in component selection and manufacture can produce excellent results with any type of transport system. The converse is also true. The purpose here is not to evaluate hypothetical merits of the various arrangements but to analyze the details of many mechanical configurations so that intelligent and efficient servicing can be accomplished.

Typical Tape Transports

The paragraphs that follow describe a full range of tape transport systems ranging from those found in professional instruments to those found in economy models. Since single-motor systems employing pulleys and belts are extensively used in present-day recorders, most attention is given to the variations found in this type of system. The initial descriptions are given in great detail to assure a thorough understanding of fundamentals. In later descriptions, attention is given mainly to that which is different and unusual.

Example 1. Ampex Models 602 and 602-2 Magnetic Tape Recorder/Reproducers (Figs. 5-1 through 5-4)

The Ampex Models 602 and 602-2 — three-head, single- and dual-channel tape recorder/reproducers; respectively — are intended for professional use. Depending upon the type of magnetic heads selected, Model 602 will record and reproduce either one or two-track tapes. Model 602-2 records and plays back two-track monophonic and stereo recordings. Model 602-2, shown in Fig. 5-1, is comprised of a tape transport unit and two identical electronic units mounted in a single case. Model 602 is essentially the same, except that it has only one electronic unit. Because of the intended professional use, these recorders do not contain either power amplifiers or loudspeakers.

Fig. 5-1 Ampex Model 602-2 two-channel professional tape recorder. Courtesy: Ampex Corp.

Fig. 5-2 Rear view of tape transport in Ampex Model 602-2. Courtesy: Ampex Corp.

Both recorders are available to operate with either 50 or 60 cycle power (117 volts, single-phase) at tape speeds of either 7½ ips (+ 2, − 4db; 40 to 15,000 cps) or 3¾ ips (+ 2, − 4 db; 40 to 8,000 cps). The recorders are available either uncased or mounted in a luggage-type portable carrying case. Accessories include plug-in input transformers, plug-in microphone preamplifiers, and a speaker-amplifier (10 watt) assembly.

General. The tape transport mechanism incorporates a single-speed synchronous motor and a system of pulleys, belts, and clutches to drive the capstan and the turntables. The three modes of tape motion (Play, Rewind, and Fast Forward) are determined by two controls located on the top panel of the tape transport. (The neutral position for each control is marked by a dot.) The bracketed numbers in this section refer to parts shown in Figs. 5-3 and 5-4.

Standby Operation. Power is applied to the drive motor when the Power switch on the front panel of the electronic assembly is turned to the On position. The capstan (7) begins to rotate immediately, being

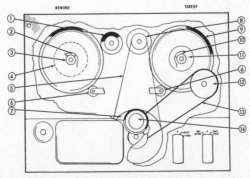

Fig. 5-3 Simplified diagram of major components of tape transport in Ampex Model 602-2. Courtesy: Ampex Corp.

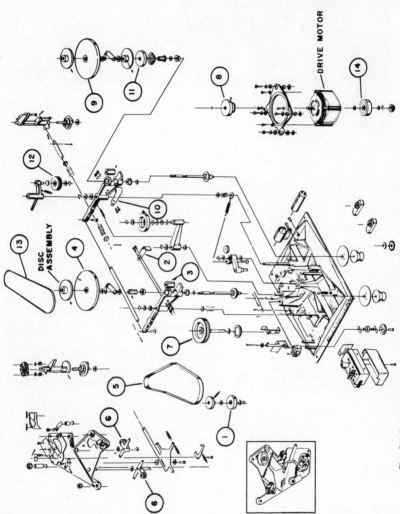

Fig. 5-4 Exploded view of tape transport in Ampex Model 602-2. Courtesy: Ampex Corp.

driven by a nylon belt (5) that runs between the motor pulley (8) and the capstan flywheel. A second belt (13) running in a groove in the capstan flywheel drives the play take-up pulley (12). The shock relief brake rollers (6) are engaged against the rubbertired fast forward and rewind clutches (9 and 4). Both turntables are motionless, and the machine is in standby condition.

Since the capstan is in motion when the machine is in the standby condition, the tape will accelerate to full play speed almost instantly when the Play switch is operated, thus producing a wow-free start.

Play Mode. When the Play control is energized, the following mechanical sequence occurs:

1. The play take-up pulley (12) and belt (13) are brought to bear on the play take-up clutch (11).

2. The shock relief brake roller (6) on the play take-up side is released from the fast forward clutch tire (9).

3. The capstan idler (14) engages the capstan (7), which drives the tape, pulling it from the tape supply turntable (that is, the rewind turntable) and feeding it to the take-up turntable, which now begins to rotate. It is especially important to understand that when the machine is operating normally in the play mode, in which the tape is clamped against the capstan by the capstan idler, the turntables are effectively isolated from each other. The take-up turntable, as its name implies, does nothing more than take up the tape fed to it by the capstan. It does not pull the tape from the tape supply turntable.

4. The shock relief brake roller (6) on the rewind side remains engaged against the rewind clutch tire (4), and slippage occurs between the clutch and disc assembly. The friction produced in this slippage and the friction produced by the rewind holdback brake (2) operating on the bakelite drum (3) provide the required holdback tension.

Rewind Mode. The Rewind-Fast Forward control cannot be operated unless the Play control is in neutral. When the Rewind-Fast Forward control is turned to Rewind:

1. Both shock relief brake rollers (6) are released.

2. The rewind idler (1) is clamped between the motor pulley (8) and the rewind clutch tire (4) and the rewind turntable is driven.

3. Holdback tension is provided by the holdback brake (10) on the take-up assembly as tape is pulled from the take-up turntable.

Fast Forward Mode. When the Rewind-Fast Forward control is turned to Fast Forward:

1. Both shock relief brake rollers (6) are released.

2. The rubber-tired fast forward clutch (9) is brought to bear on the motor pulley (8) and drives the take-up turntable.

3. Holdback tension is produced by the holdback brake (2) on the rewind assembly.

Example 2.   Ekotape Series 500, Webster Electric Co. (Figs. 5-5 through 5-7)

The Webster Electric "Ekotape" 500 series magnetic tape recorders are designed for audio-visual applications in the educational field. With this use in mind they feature lightness for easy portability, compactness for minimum space requirement on a desk, and simple controls for easy student use. These units were illustrated in Chapter 4, Figs. 4-12 and 4-13.

All models in this series contain a tape transport driven by a single motor. Model 500 weighs 22 pounds and is equipped with a large-handled carrying case; it has a fully transistorized preamplifier and amplifier for resistance to shock during transportation. It is a single-channel, half-track unit, has record and monitor-playback heads, and operates at 3¾ and 7½ ips. Model 510-1 (Fig. 4-12) is a two-channel, half-track, two-head unit; it is intended for recording the program or lesson on one track and permitting the student to record his response on the second track. Both the program and response can be played back simultaneously for evaluation and correction. Except for the track and head arrangement, other features (including weight) are similar to Model 500.

Webster educational equipment assemblies such as a teaching console, student booths, and a mobile teaching laboratory make use of other, similar tape recorders in the 500 series. These include: Model 520, which is an uncased unit similar to Model 500; Models 540 and 542, which are two-channel, two-track tape decks; Model 642, which is a two-track deck employing RCA type cartridges; plus accessory amplifiers and program selectors.

Tape Transport Assembly. The 500 series tape transport mechanism (Figs. 5-5 through 5-7) uses a single-speed motor and a system of pulleys, drive idlers, and clutches to drive the capstan and reel shaft assemblies. A single central control knob selects the three modes of tape movement: Play, Fast Forward, or Rewind, plus a neutral or Stop position. The record mode is selected by a separate switch with a safety interlock feature to prevent accidental erasure.

Tape movement in the play/record positions is governed by the movement of the tape between the capstan idler (pinch roller) and the capstan (flywheel and shaft assembly). Tape speed is governed solely by the rotation of the flywheel and shaft when one of two tape speeds is selected with the speed change control.

Standby Mode. Power is applied to the drive motor when the speed change control is turned to either one of two speeds, − 3¾ or 7½ ips. The capstan immediately begins to rotate, being driven by a drive idler positioned between the motor pulley and flywheel. The capstan's rotation is determined by one of two drive idlers selected by the speed change control.

The drive idlers are identical; in contact with the large or small

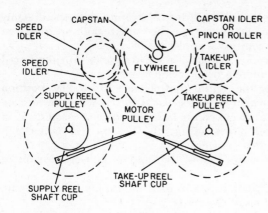

Fig. 5-5 Major components of tape transport in Play mode, Ekotape Series 500. Courtesy: Webster Electric Co.

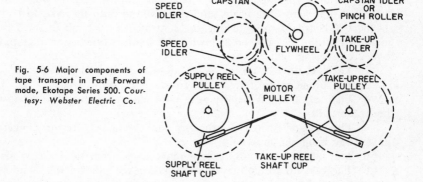

Fig. 5-6 Major components of tape transport in Fast Forward mode, Ekotape Series 500. Courtesy: Webster Electric Co.

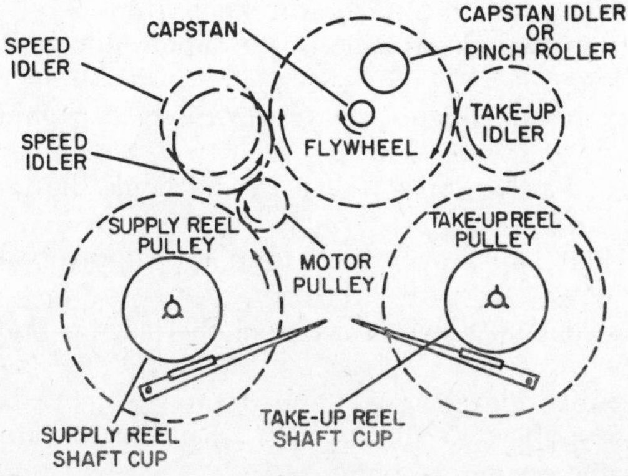

Fig. 5-7 Major components of tape transport in Rewind mode, Ekotape Series 500. Courtesy: Webster Electric Co.

circumference of the motor pulley, they determine tape speed. Only one idler contacts the motor pulley in either speed. Both are retracted when the speed change control is turned to Off.

A fan attached to the lower shaft of the drive motor provides forced draft to cool the motor and electronic components.

Play Mode. Turning the central control knob to the Play position will almost instantly provide full tape speed as the capstan is in motion. The following mechanical action occurs in rapid sequence (see Fig. 5-5):

1. The take-up idler moves against the take-up reel pulley and rotates the take-up reel shaft assembly.

2. The pinch roller moves against the capstan, putting the tape in motion.

3. The take-up reel shaft cup, and then the supply reel shaft cup, are retracted from their respective brake pads.

4. The tape-off switch plastic arm is pulled in and holds the tape against the switch guide post.

5. The pressure fingers move the tape into contact with the heads. In this manner, the tape is pulled from the supply reel, through the tape-off switch, across the heads, and then wound onto the take-up reel.

Fast Forward Mode. Turning the central control knob to the Fast Forward position sets up the following mechanical interaction in rapid sequence (see Fig. 5-6):

1. The take-up reel pulley moves away from the take-up idler.

2. The pinch roller moves away from the capstan.

3. The take-up and supply reel cups momentarily move against the brake pads.

4. The tape-off switch plastic arm and the head pressure fingers move away from the tape.

5. The take-up and supply cups move away from the brake pads.

6. The take-up reel pulley moves against the take-up idler and is driven by the flywheel while the supply reel pulley floats free. In this manner, the take-up reel pulley and take-up shaft assembly pull the tape from the supply reel.

Rewind Mode. Turning the central control knob from Stop to Rewind moves the tape from the take-up side to the supply side in the following sequence (see Fig. 5-7):

1. The take-up reel shaft cup is depressed against the take-up brake pad.

2. The tape-off switch plastic arm is pulled in and holds the tape against the tape-off switch guide post.

3. The supply reel shaft cup moves away from the supply brake pad.

4. The take-up reel shaft cup moves away from the take-up brake pad and floats freely.

5. The supply reel pulley moves against the rewind disc and tire assembly above the motor pulley. In this manner, the tape is pulled from the take-up reel by the rewind (supply) reel.

Stop Position.

1. When moving into the Stop position from Rewind, Play, or Fast Forward, the mechanical sequence is the reverse of that described in the preceding pagagraphs.

2. The Stop position retracts the tape-off switch plastic arm, head pressure fingers, and pinch roller assembly and allows both brake pads to apply pressure to the reel shaft cups.

Record Mode (Models 500 and 520).

1. On these models the record switch and safety interlock are mechanically linked to the control-cam assembly to prevent accidental erasure of the tape in the Play, Fast Forward, or Rewind position.

2. The record switch is equipped with a spring-loaded interlock slide to prevent its being accidentally actuated.

Record Mode (Models 510, 540, and 542).

1. The RECORD modes of these models are not mechanically linked to the tape transport mechanism. However, a safety interlock feature is provided to prevent accidental erasure of the lower channels.

Example 3. RCA Tape Cartridge Recorders, RCA Sales Corp. (Figs. 5-8 through 5-11)

RCA Tape Cartridge Recorders employ the tape cartridge previously described in conjunction with the tape transport assembly to be described here. All models employ a single-motor transport, a single record/playback head, and a single erase head. All operate at $3\frac{3}{4}$ ips (50 to 15,000 cps) and $1\frac{7}{8}$ ips (50 to 6,000 cps). Differences between the various models are mainly concerned with mono/stereo operation, microphone and speaker arrangements, controls, and cabinet design. Model 1YB1 is a four-track monaural unit with a neon recording indicator and Model 1YB29A is similar with a magic eye indicator. Model 3YD1 is a four-track stereo/monaural unit with a magic eye indicator and has two recording preamplifiers, two playback amplifiers, one speaker in the cabinet, and one speaker in the cabinet lid. Model 1YC1 is similar to 3YD1 and has two recording preamplifiers, one playback amplifier, and one speaker; an external amplifier and speaker are required for stereo playback.

Tape Transports TCT-3 and TCT-3A. Models TCT-3 and TCT-3A are high-fidelity, dual-speed, semi-automatic tape transports designed to use RCA Victor tape cartridges (see Fig. 5-8). These transports are capable of making and playing back stereophonic or monophonic recordings at tape speeds of $1\frac{7}{8}$ ips or $3\frac{3}{4}$ ips when connected to the appropriate equipment.

Tape movement is controlled by the Rewind-Stop-Play knob with the additional provision of automatic shut-off when the tape is completely transported from one hub of the cartridge to the other in either direction. The transport is also equipped with an automatic nonerase interlock which prevents the accidental erasure of prerecorded tape.

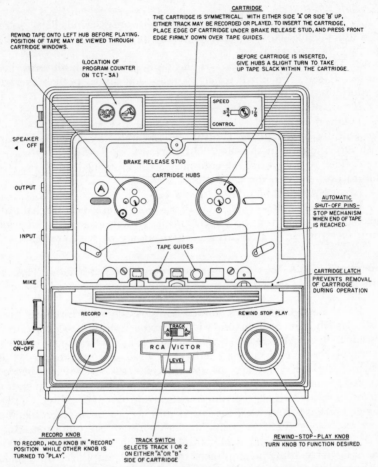

Fig. 5-8 RCA Victor TCT-3 and TCT-3A tape transport, showing controls and summary of operating instructions. *Courtesy: RCA Sales Corp.*

Tape cartridges are handled as easily as phonograph records since the threading of tape into the reels is eliminated. Cartridges are available with either blank or four-track prerecorded tape. Blank cartridges contain approximately 600 feet of 1/4-inch magnetic tape.

To play a tape, it is necessary only to place the loaded cartridge on the transport with the desired side face up, set the Track selector switch, and turn the Play knob. Two of the four tracks are used simultaneously for a stereophonic recording, or one track at a time for a monophonic recording. To play a succeeding tape track, after each automatic shut-off, simply turn the cartridge over, set the Track selector switch (if necessary), and turn the Play knob. At a tape speed of 1 7/8 ips, a fully loaded cartridge will provide either two hours of stereophonic recording or four hours of monophonic recording when all tracks are used. At a tape speed of 3¾ inches per second, a full cartridge will provide either one hour of stereophonic recording or two hours of monophonic recording.

The model TCT-3A differs from model TCT-3 in that it contains a digital type counter, to help locate desired sections of the tape, and a Tuning Eye level indicator instead of a neon lamp.

Automatic Shut Off. The TCT-3, -3A mechanism (Figs. 5-9 through 5-11) is designed to shut off automatically when the tape is completely transported from one hub of the cartridge to the other. This is accomplished by moving the tape across shut-off pins that "sense" the tape tension. Each pin is attached to a lever that is part of a toggle link system. When the Rewind-Stop-Play knob is placed in either the Play or Rewind position, a control pivot assembly moves past center and the shut-off pins are placed in their operating or "sensing" positions. As the tape moves from one hub to the other, a slight force is exerted upon the shut-off pins; this force is insufficient, however, to trip the shut-off linkage. When the end of the tape is reached, the force acting upon the shut-off pins is greatly increased as a result of the tape's being anchored to the cartridge hubs. This increased force moves the shut-off pins to their Off (loading) position and trips the toggle system, causing the Rewind-Stop-Play knob to return to the Stop position. Simultaneously, the rewind and brake lever (43) applies a brake to the left spindle, and a tab on this lever contacts the motor switch (44), shutting off the motor.

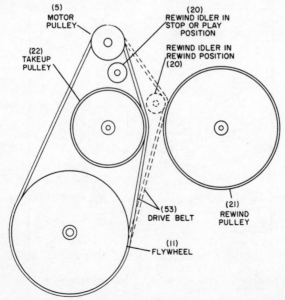

Fig. 5-9 Major components of tape transport, RCA Victor TCT-3 and TCT-3A. *Courtesy: RCA Sales Corp.*

Play. When the Rewind-Stop-Play knob is placed in the Play position, the motor switch (44) is closed, the brake (43) is released from the left pulley (21), the pressure roller (33) is pressed firmly against the capstan (11), and the pressure pads (88A) press the tape firmly against the erase and record heads (57 and 55). The toggle link assembly is also actuated, moving the shut-off pins (43B and 46A) into their "sensing" position.

The driving force is transmitted from the motor to the flywheel and capstan assembly (11) through the drive belt (53). The same drive belt also transmits the driving force to the take-up pulley (22), which, in turn, drives its turntable (15) through the clutch assembly.

Rewind. When the Rewind-Stop-Play knob is placed in the Rewind position, the motor switch (44) is closed, the brake (43) is released from the left pulley (21), and the rewind idler (20) pushes the drive belt (53) away from the take-up pulley (22) and against the rewind pulley (21). The toggle link assembly is also actuated, moving the shut-off pins (43A and 46A) into their "sensing" positions.

Stop. When the Rewind-Stop-Play knob is returned to the Stop posi-

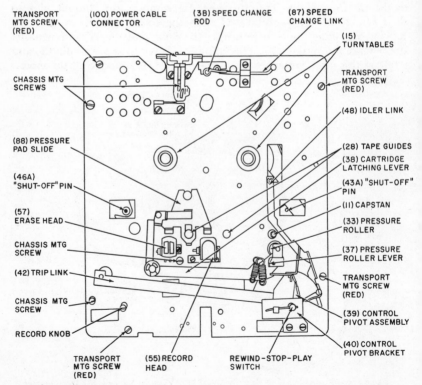

Fig. 5-10 Tape transport components below top deck, RCA Victor TCT-3 and TCT-3A.
Courtesy: RCA Sales Corp.

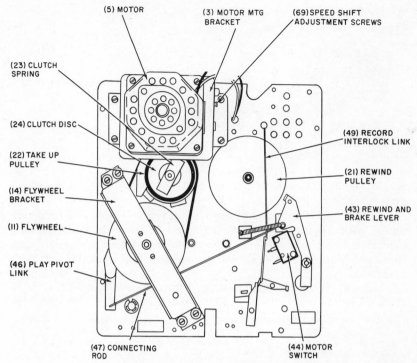

(5) MOTOR

(3) MOTOR MTG BRACKET

(69) SPEED SHIFT ADJUSTMENT SCREWS

(23) CLUTCH SPRING

(24) CLUTCH DISC

(22) TAKE UP PULLEY

(14) FLYWHEEL BRACKET

(11) FLYWHEEL

(46) PLAY PIVOT LINK

(49) RECORD INTERLOCK LINK

(21) REWIND PULLEY

(43) REWIND AND BRAKE LEVER

(47) CONNECTING ROD

(44) MOTOR SWITCH

Fig. 5-11 Bottom view of tape transport components, RCA Victor TCT-3 and TCT-3A. Courtesy: RCA Sales Corp.

tion, power to the motor is turned off, and the brake pad (43B) is applied to the rewind pulley (21). Simultaneously, the shut-off pins (43A and 46A) move to their "off" (loading) positions, the idler linkage returns to its neutral position, the pressure pads (88A) move away from the heads, and the pressure roller (33) disengages from the capstan.

Example 4.   Heathkit Models AD-22 and AD-72, Heath Co. (Figs. 5-12 through 5-14)

These recorders are supplied in kit form for assembly by the purchaser. Both units record and play back four-track stereo/monaural recordings at $3\frac{3}{4}$ and $7\frac{1}{2}$ ips, and both employ the same tape transport. Model AD-22 includes the complete single-motor tape transport mechanism, two heads, and two record/playback preamplifiers. This unit adds a tape recording facility to existing disc stereo systems having two amplifiers with speakers. In its slow and fast tape speeds, its frequency response is 40 to 10,000 cps and 40 to 15,000 cps, respectively. Model AD-72 is similar but includes two 2-watt playback amplifiers with monitoring

Fig. 5-12 Heathkit Model AD-72 Recorder. *Courtesy: Heath Co.*

speakers and a cabinet. In its slow and fast tape speeds, its frequency response is 50 to 10,000 cps and 50 to 15,000 cps, respectively.

Mechanism. The tape deck mechanism uses a single-speed induction motor, with a system of pulleys, belts, and idlers to drive the capstan, turntables, and the counter. The Play-Record and Rewind-Forward controls, each with a Neutral position, provide the four modes of tape deck operation.

Neutral. When the Power switch is turned on, the motor starts to drive the capstan through the capstan drive belt. This belt runs between

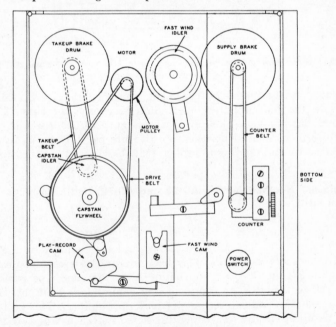

Fig. 5-13 Major components of tape transport, Heathkit Models AD-22 and AD-72, seen from below. *Courtesy: Heath Co.*

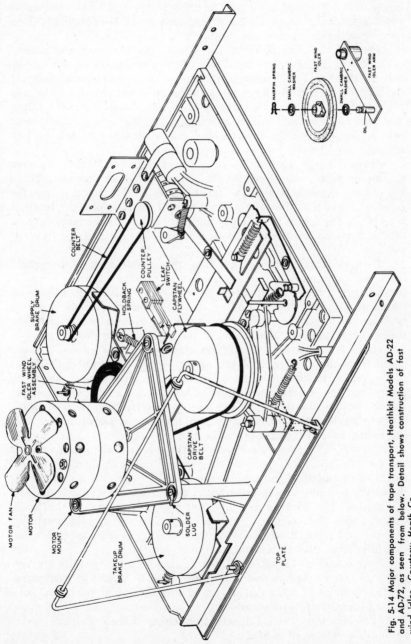

Fig. 5-14 Major components of tape transport, Heathkit Models AD-22 and AD-72, as seen from below. Detail shows construction of fast wind idler. Courtesy: Heath Co.

the motor pulley and the capstan flywheel. With the Play-Record and Rewind-Forward controls in Neutral, no part of the deck is operating, except the motor and capstan. The rubber-tired fast wind idler is engaged against the supply brake drum, each brake is applied to its respective brake drum, and the turntables are motionless.

Play. In the Play position, the take-up brake releases the take-up brake drum, and the play-record cam allows the tension on the take-up belt to increase. The capstan idler engages the capstan, thus clamping the tape between them. The capstan then pulls the tape from the supply reel and feeds it to the take-up reel, which now begins to rotate. The take-up turntable is driven by the capstan idler through the take-up belt. A lubricant on the capstan idler pulley provides the take-up belt slippage required for proper take-up tension.

Speed Change. Capstan speed is determined by the ratio between the motor pulley diameter and the capstan flywheel diameter. When the capstan drive belt is in the small groove of the motor pulley, the capstan is driven at the correct speed to pull the tape past the heads at the rate of $3\frac{3}{4}$ ips. When the capstan drive belt is in the larger groove of the motor pulley, the capstan then moves the tape past the heads at the rate of $7\frac{1}{2}$ ips.

Forward. In the Forward position, the capstan idler is disengaged from the capstan, thus freeing the tape. The take-up brake drum is pressed against the outer rim of the motor pulley. This drives the take-up turntable forward, thereby pulling the tape from the supply reel at a high rate of speed. Tension on the supply turntable is produced by the supply brake pressing lightly against the supply brake drum.

Rewind. In the Rewind position, the take-up brake drum is disengaged from the outer rim of the motor pulley. The rubber-tired rim of the fast wind idler is engaged between the metal rim of the motor pulley and the supply brake drum. This drives the rewind turntable, thereby pulling the tape from the take-up reel at a high rate of speed. Tension on the take-up turntable is produced by the take-up brake pressing lightly against the take-up brake drum.

Counter. The counter is driven by the supply brake drum through the counter belt. The speed of the counter pulley is directly proportional to the speed of the supply turntable. This permits accurate editing of the tape and also locating a particular recorded selection quickly.

Brakes. The brake arms, their felt pads acting against the brake drums, apply the necessary braking when switching from Forward to Neutral and from Rewind to Neutral. Braking is also applied when switching from Play to Neutral.

Interlock. The Play-Record and Rewind-Forward controls are mechanically interlocked so that one control must be placed in its Neutral position before the other can be placed in either of its operating positions. This safety feature guards against tape breakage that would occur if the machine was switched directly from either of the high-speed modes to the Play or Record mode.

Example 5.   Cipher VII, Inter-Mark Corp. (Figs. 5-15 through 5-19)

The Cipher VII is a 45-pound unit that records and plays back four-track stereo/monaural recordings. This recorder has all standard features including two detachable speakers, two VU record indicators, and two tone controls. The single-motor tape transport has three operating speeds: 7½ ips (35 to 15,000 cps), 3¾ ips (35 to 12,000 cps), and 1⅞ ips (25 to 7,000 cps).

Tape Transport Assembly. The tape transport mechanism incorporates a single-speed induction motor and a system of idler pulleys and belt. Five modes of tape motion (REW, Stop, Play, I.S., and F.F.) are selected by a control knob located on the top panel of the tape recorder. Major components are shown in Fig. 5-15.

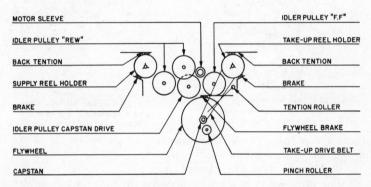

Fig. 5-15 Cipher VII tape transport components (shown in Stop mode). *Courtesy: Inter-Mark*

Playback Mode. When the control knob is in the Play position (Fig. 5-16), the following mechanical sequence occurs:

1. The idler pulley for the capstan drive engages with the flywheel and the motor sleeve, and the capstan begins to rotate.

2. The brake shoes on the supply reel side and the take-up reel side are released from these reel holders.

3. The take-up reel holder begins to rotate. The pinch roller engages the capstan, which drives the tape, pulling it from the supply reel holder and feeding it to the take-up reel holder. In the playback position, the take-up reel does not take up more tape than is fed to it by the capstan, and slip occurs between the nylon pulley on the flywheel and the belt.

4. The brake operates on the supply reel holder and provides the back tension.

I.S. (Instant Stop) Mode. The pinch roller releases from the capstan, and the tape ceases to move. The position of the various components is shown in Fig. 5-17.

F.F. (Fast Forward) Mode. When the control knob is in the F.F.

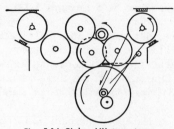

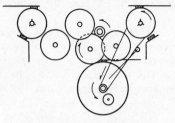

Fig. 5-16 Cipher VII tape transport components in Play mode. Courtesy: Inter-Mark Corp

Fig. 5-17 Cipher VII tape transport components in Stop mode. Courtesy: Inter-Mark Corp.

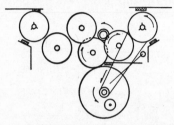

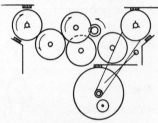

Fig. 5-18 Cipher VII tape transport components in Fast Forward mode. Courtesy: Inter-Mark Corp.

Fig. 5-19 Cipher VII tape transport components in Rewind mode. Courtesy: Inter-Mark Corp.

position, the position of the components is as shown in Fig. 5-18. The following mechanical events take place:

1. Both brake shoes are released.

2. The idler pulley is clamped between the take-up reel holder and the motor sleeve, the take-up reel holder is driven, and the tape is moved at high speed.

3. Back tension is provided by the back tension brake on the supply reel holder.

REW (Fast Rewind) Mode. When the control knob is turned to REW, the following events take place, as shown in Fig. 5-19:

1. Both brake shoes are released.

2. The idler pulleys for rewind are clamped between the supply reel holder and the motor sleeve and drive the supply reel holder. Then the tape is rewound at high speed.

3. Back tension is produced by the back tension brake on the take-up reel holder.

Example 6.   Stancil-Hoffman Minitape, Model M9 (Fig. 5-20)

The recorders described up to this point have all employed a single a-c motor with a variety of mechanical drive mechanisms to provide the various tape transport functions. Other arrangements are used in present-day recorders and will be described in this and the following examples. The Minitape, Model M9, is specifically designed to provide high-

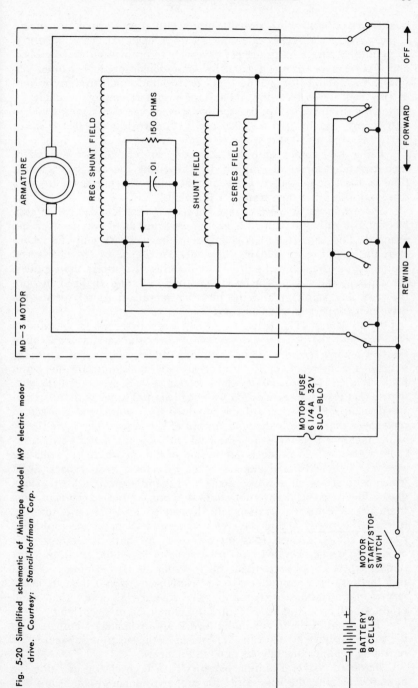

Fig. 5-20 Simplified schematic of Minitape Model M9 electric motor drive. Courtesy: Stancil-Hoffman Corp.

quality recordings with a portable unit. This transistorized instrument is packaged in a carrying case and is battery operated. Total weight is 13 pounds. Separate heads are employed for recording and playing back, and a permanent magnet is used for erase. Single or dual-channel versions are available for making one- or two-track monaural recordings or two-track stereo recordings. The tape transport employs a single d-c motor for driving the tape at any one selected speed of 7½ ips (50 to 10,000 cps), 3¾ ips (50 to 5,000 cps), 1⅞ ips (150 to 4,000 cps), or 15/16 ips (150 to 3,000 cps).

Using a d-c motor simplifies the tape transport in that reversal of tape direction can be accomplished by reversing the armature connections to the voltage source. Conventional pulley arrangements are used to accomplish other tape transport functions.

Speed Change. A speed change between 7½ ips and 3¾ ips is possible because only the pinchwheel and the capstan drive member are changed. The equalization is changed in the playback amplifier; however, the record curve remains the same. To change to 1⅞ tape speed requires an exchange of the drive motor pulley, an intermediate pulley, the capstan, and the pinchwheel. Equalization is also changed in both the recording amplifier and the playback amplifier. At all speeds, the drive motor operates at 3,600 rpm.

Drive Motor. The drive motor has been designed for maximum efficiency and the best regulation possible over the varying load conditions of a tape recorder, along with the varying voltages of a storage battery. The drive motor is constructed with two shunt and one series field windings. It incorporates tight tolerances and precision ball bearings so that it will operate over a wide temperature range without serious speed change. Speed regulation is obtained by a centrifugal contact arrangement that controls the field current of the motor. The basic theory of the motor is that increasing the field will slow the motor. This is because a greater field produces more lines of flux in which the armature revolves. This additional amount of flux creates a greater back EMF, which counteracts the supply voltage, and the motor consequently slows down. The centrifugal governor closes the contact above 3,600 rpm. The frequency of contact operation will depend on many factors; however, it will fall between 50 and 100 cycles per second. A motor speed of 3,600 rpm was chosen because it is an easy speed to check and adjust. Any neon lamp or a-c operated glow tube at 60 cycles would produce a stationary stroboscopic pattern of the governor. If the Minitape is used in a territory where only 50 cycles is available, it would then be necessary to use an audio oscillator or some commercial device that could produce a 60-cycle frequency to fire the glow tube or neon lamp.

The drain of the motor under load is approximately 1 ampere with the battery voltage at 10.0 volts. The drain of the electronic system while recording is approximately 50 to 60 milliamperes.

Batteries. Nickel cadmium batteries have been chosen as being the most reliable and the best suited for the environmental conditions and operating conditions to which the Minitape will be subjected. Eight cells make up the battery, which has a 4 ampere hour capacity, affording at least 4 hours of operating power. Each cell has a nominal voltage of 1.2 to 1.25 volts. The battery in its full-charged condition will have a voltage of around 11.5 volts. In a discharged condition, it will drop to 9.0 or slightly lower with no load. This operating voltage range was selected so that the battery could be charged by the cigarette lighter connection of a standard 12-volt car battery. The lead-acid type of battery used in automobiles has a relatively broad voltage range. If a 12-volt system had been used, there would be many instances wherein it would not be possible to charge the recorder battery from the automobile battery; however, with the lower voltage, it is possible to charge the recorder battery by floating it across an automobile battery even while the engine is not running.

Example 7. Transmagnemite Model 612, Amplifier Corporation of America (Fig. 5-21)

This tape recorder is designed for portable professional use under rugged field conditions and in locations where sources of electricity and batteries may not be available most of the time. Transistorization and the elimination of storage batteries for driving the tape transport result in a 15-pound unit that can produce professional-quality monaural recordings for extended periods of time.

The concept of the design is to employ a high-quality spring motor for driving the tape transport. Thus the operator supplies the major part of the energy for operating the recorder, and small, dry rechargeable batteries operate the electronics for 125 hours before recharge becomes necessary. Tape reels are 5 inches in diameter, and capstan drive is employed. A single record/playback head is used with a permanent

Fig. 5-21 Transmagnemite Model 612, a transistorized recorder with a spring motor. Courtesy: Amplifier Corporation of America.

magnet for erasing. Outstanding features of the various models are as follows:

Model No.	Tape speed (ips)	Tracks	Frequency response	Winding interval (min)
612-A	15/16	2	300– 2,500	30
612-B	1⅞	2	100– 3,000	15
612-C	3¾	2	50– 7,500	7½
612-TD	7½	2	50–10,000	6
612-SD	7½	1	50–10,000	6
612-E	15	1	50–15,000	3

Two-, three- and four-speed models are also available. All versions are available in 17-pound models with a VU recording level meter.

Tape Transport Features. The tape transport employs capstan drive and a pulley-and-belt system similar in concept to previously described systems of this type. Only the differences will be mentioned here.

The heart of the tape transport is a special spring motor driven by two helically coiled springs mechanically connected in parallel. All spring surfaces are highly polished and silicone-lubricated to assure smooth unwinding. A balanced flyball governor provides constant speed operation and automatically compensates for changes in ambient temperature. The elimination of electrical motors and governors provides extremely low noise operation (less than 0.25-microvolt equivalent noise input), which is superior to many professional studio recorders.

The high-inertia doughnut flywheel shown mounted above the front panel is much more effective than the smaller disc-type flywheels normally employed in recorders. The mass of the flywheel is concentrated in the large-diameter doughnut, where it supplies maximum momentum and assures exceptionally low flutter. Since the flywheel is removed during transport, the capstan bearing and shaft are protected from damage that might result from vibration and mechanical shock applied to the flywheel. Self-lubricating ball bearings are used on the supply and take-up reel shafts within the pressure roller and around the capstan shaft.

Example 8. Westinghouse Model H-28R1 (Figs. 5-22 and 5-23)

This portable recorder is completely transistorized and battery-operated. It is a single-channel (monaural) two-track unit with a self-contained speaker and a permanently wired-in microphone. Reel diameter is 3 inches. Two drive motors drive the reels directly, and no capstan is employed.

The recorder employs a minimum of components to achieve

simplicity and light weight. Direct-current bias is used both for recording and erase. One combination record/play head is used together with an erase head. Tape speed is adjustable and unspecified, and frequency response is from 300 to 4,500 cps. A VU meter is used as a record-level indicator.

General Features. The tape transport makes use of two d-c motors and does not use a capstan. One motor drives the supply reel turntable and is used only in rewind. The other motor drives the take-up reel and is used in Record, Playback, and Fast Forward. Both motors are attached to spring-loaded mountings and are moved so that their shafts bear against rubber rims attached to the reel turntables.

Play and Record. In both these operations the function selector knob actuates the tape pressure pads so as to hold the tape against the heads. The wind motor shaft is pressed against the take-up reel, and the motor can be turned on and off with the microphone switch. The rewind motor shaft is disconnected from the supply reel.

Microphone switch SW2 and remote-control jack J2 are connected in series with wind motor M1, speed-control rheostat R20, and fast-forward switch SW1, and are connected to the motor battery by contacts 2 and 3 of SW4. When SW1 is set to Fast, cell B3 is connected in series with 1.5-volt battery B1-B2 in the wind motor circuit. Using this Fast (fast forward) position doubles the speed of the wind motor in both playback and record. The speed control R20 adjusts the speed of the wind motor in both playback and record. This compensates for battery wear and aging; the speed control is normally left at its mid-position for recording and is adjusted for normal sound during playback.

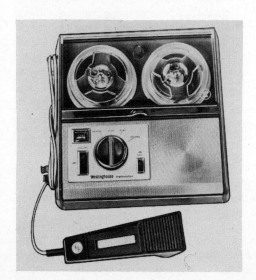

Fig. 5-22 Westinghouse Model H-28R1 all-transistor, battery-operated tape recorder. *Courtesy: Westinghouse Electric Corp.*

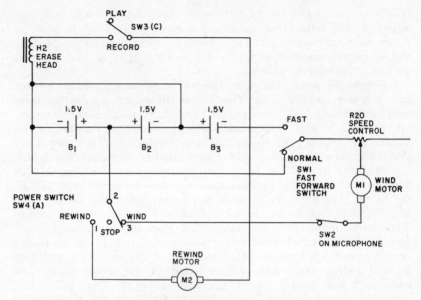

Fig. 5-23 Simplified schematic of electric motor drive circuits in Westinghouse Model H-28R1 tape recorder. *Courtesy: Westinghouse Electric Corp.*

Rewind Function. When the function selector knob is set at Rewind, battery B1-B2-B3 is connected to rewind motor M2 by contacts 1 and 2 of power switch SW4. The wind motor is moved so that its shaft no longer contacts the rubber drive rim of the take-up reel. The rewind motor is moved so that its shaft bears against the rubber rim that drives the supply reel. These mechanical and electrical operations drive the supply reel in the rewind direction at fast speed.

Stop Function. When the function selector knob is set at Stop, power is disconnected from all circuits. Due to the use of transistors, the electronics are operable as soon as the knob is set to either the Record or Play positions.

Example 9. Viking Model 96, Viking of Minneapolis, Inc. (Figs. 5-24 and 5-25)

Multi-Motor Drives. The three-motor drive system was once very popular in professional recorders and is still used to some extent in quality units. Systems of this type can operate without pulleys, clutches, and brakes when so designed.

In an arrangement of this type the capstan is usually directly driven by a synchronous motor running at 1,800 rpm or 900 rpm. Such a speed change, and even additional changes, are accomplished by switching the motor windings from four-to eight-pole or other configurations. Clutches are not necessary to supply the required slippage. The supply and take-up reels are each driven by their own motor. Slippage at the take-up reel is provided by operating that motor in a stalled condition so that the back-pull of the tape coming from the capstan is sufficient to restrain the motor from turning faster than required. Brakes are also unnecessary since removing the voltage and shorting the motor windings provide effective electro-dynamic braking.

Viking Model 96. The Viking Model 96 is a rugged, three-motor transport designed for commercial, broadcast, and critical recording applications. This professional tape transport features simplified operating controls, excellent tape handling capability, exceptionally good flutter and wow characteristics, and a wide variety of head combinations for quarter-track, half-track, and full-track recording on quarter-inch tape. The 96 transport combines a hysteresis synchronous motor capstan drive and the 10½-inch reel capacity required for commercial recording. A variety of matching magnetic head combinations, preamplifiers, recording amplifiers, and record/playback amplifiers are available for use with this transport. The Viking Retro-Matic 220, which employs a transport based upon similar concepts, has a frequency response of 20 to 25,000 cps at 7½ ips and 20 to 15,000 cps at 3¾ ips.

Controls. The 96 tape transport is controlled by means of four telephone-type lever or "key" switches. From left to right, these are: the "Reel Size Selector," "Speed Selector," "Play-Cue," and "Fast-Forward, Rewind" controls. Time delay circuits provide for virtually foolproof operation of the control switches. For example, the unit may be switched out of rewind and simultaneously placed in the for-

Fig. 5-24 Viking Model 96 Professional Tape Transport with two RP62 VU recording playback amplifiers. *Courtesy: Viking of Minneapolis.*

Fig. 5-25 Rear view of Viking Model 96 tape transport, showing details of three-motor drive. Courtesy: Viking of Minneapolis.

ward position without danger of lowering the capstan roller to engage the tape. The capstan roller engages only after the reels have come to a stop.

Tape Speeds. Selection of either of two speeds is accomplished electrically. A lever switch permits selection of 7½ and 15, 3¾ and 7½, or 1⅞ and 3¾ ips, depending upon the diameter of the drive pulley provided. Any of the three drive pulleys is available as standard equipment. Additional pulleys may be purchased and may be installed by the user, permitting coverage of the four speeds.

Capstan Drive. The performance of the Model 96 is mainly due to the heavy-duty capstan drive motor that does not drive the capstan directly. Instead, a 3½-pound dynamically-balanced capstan flywheel is driven through a triple-belt drive from the hysteresis synchronous capstan drive motor. Flutter and wow is held to 1/10 of 1% (rms) at 7½ ips on standard production units. Long-term speed regulation is 0.5%.

Take-up and Rewind. The Model 96 handles 10½-inch and all smaller reel sizes. Six-pole, induction motors drive the take-up and supply reels. A special circuit provides smooth tape starting by momentarily applying over two times the torque that is required for normal running. A single three-position switch selects optimum tape tension and differentials for dynamic braking. Reel sizes may be inter-mixed. Rewind and fast-forward time for 2,400 feet of tape (10½-inch reel) is 70 seconds. Dynamic braking provides fast-forward to stop, or fast-rewind to stop, in less than 2 seconds. Complete interlock protection prevents engaging the capstan pressure roller while the tape is moving at high speed and also prevents damage that might otherwise result from tape breaking, or from a power failure.

Reel Mountings. The NAB hubs for mounting 10½-inch reels retract to mount standard 7- and 5-inch reels on the reel hub shafts. Precision-machined aluminum reel retainers are provided.

Tape Break and Fail-Safe Switch. A photoelectric fail-safe device automatically stops the transport in the event that tape breaks or is removed from the heads. A transparent tape section of semi-transparent leader tape can be used for jump programming and fast cueing with modified switching.

Remote Control. A connector is provided for remote switches to control play-stop and fast forward-stop-rewind functions. A second connector permits connecting external circuits for integrated control of associated electronic equipment. Remote control of all functions can be accomplished by means of one single-pole, single-throw and one single-pole, double-throw center-off switch.

Plug-In Control Boxes. All major transport control relays are contained in a 'plug-in" relay control box. This box can easily be removed. While a failure of the control relays is not considered a routine possibility, this feature becomes important in applications where lost time is costly. Stocking of a spare control box eliminates the need for a stand-by recorder.

Chapter 6

TAPE RECORDING CIRCUITRY

Since the basic electronic requirements of magnetic tape recording systems include amplification, equalization, and reproduction, they are similar to those of other types of sound recording arrangements. The block diagram of Fig. 6-1 shows the basic electronic components used in modern magnetic recording systems. As the theory behind most of these has already been explained in previous chapters, this chapter is devoted to the details of different system configurations and their individual circuits.

Many variations in arrangement and circuit details are found because of the attempts to make high-fidelity systems approach perfection of reproduction. In contrast, economy and portable models employ often ingenious techniques to achieve acceptable reproduction with minimum complexity. Examples ranging between these extremes will be described here.

Physical Construction

At the present time the physical construction of tape recorder electronic systems is in a state of change. In the field of portable instruments, the trend is almost completely to total transistorization, printed circuit boards, and battery operation. In contrast, many high-quality instruments for home and studio use still employ heavyweight metal chasses, wired circuit boards, and vacuum tubes.

Most recorders employ construction techniques between these extremes. The quality of any particular instrument cannot be determined by its adherence to ultraconservative construction or by its acceptance of the most modern techniques. As always, performance and reliability depend upon sound engineering and quality control in manufacture. Desirable physical features of tape recorder electronic units are reviewed in the paragraphs that follow.

Sectionalized Construction. Isolation of preamplifiers, oscillators, and power stages by sectional construction permits rapid replacement and causes fewer interruptions in service while the defective component

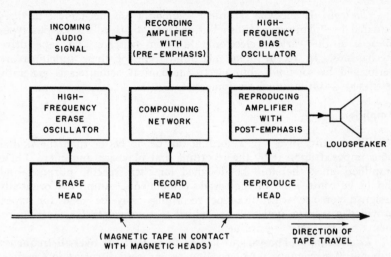

Fig. 6-1 Basic electronic and electromechanical components of a magnetic-recording system.

is being repaired. Rapid service is further assisted by plug-in construction of electronic units. Ease of access to the interior of the electronics section is a prime consideration.

Weight. Weight reduction is important in portable units. This is achieved readily by complete transistorization and the use of printed circuit boards. Professional portable systems are often divided between two carrying cases: one for the tape transport and the second for the electronics. This distributes the carrying weight and reduces transmission of hum and mechanical vibration from the drive system to the amplifiers.

Shielding. The requirements for shielding are considerable. Not only must magnetic heads be shielded from each other, but the strong fields of erase heads must be confined. Motors must be well shielded to prevent hum pick-up, and special precautions are required in three-motor units because physical separation is difficult to achieve in such cases.

Shock Mounting. Most units contain both the tape transport and the amplifiers in the same cabinet. Consequently, shock mounting of the mechanical components is necessary to prevent physical transmission of machine vibrations to the high-gain amplifier stages where microphonics could result.

Ventilation. Although fan blades are generally attached to tape recorder motors, adequate venting is required to assure proper cooling. Supplementary forced-air cooling is sometimes necessary, particularly in custom installations where the electronics are mounted in furniture-like cabinets.

Controls. Home-type recorders commonly use mechanical linkages actuated by "piano-keys," push buttons, or "joysticks" of various types to actuate the various electronic function switches and tape drive mechanisms. In recent home machines some of these functions are performed by solenoids, but electro-mechanical actuation is generally restricted to professional equipment.

Amplifiers

The quality of a tape recording can be no better than the limitations imposed upon it by the recording and playback amplifier. These amplifiers must therefore be designed for their specific purposes and should be constructed of high-grade components. Amplifiers originally designed for use with disk-type recordings may be used for tapes, provided corrective networks are added to compensate for the requirements of magnetic recording.

Equalization. The various factors that affect the over-all frequency response of a magnetic tape-recording system were discussed in Chapters 3 and 4. Correction must be made for the rise in signal amplitude in the mid-frequency range and the rapid drop-off at higher frequencies. This correction, or equalization, is accomplished in various ways by different manufacturers.

Response correction accomplished during recording is called *pre-emphasis,* while that provided during playback is called *post-emphasis.* The equalizers that accomplish the required correction are essentially high-and-low-pass filters, often adjustable to the requirements of individual taste. Although these filters can be used to attenuate the undesired frequency band (permitting subsequent amplification of only the desired frequencies), they are sometimes used in frequency-selective positive feedback circuits that supply higher amplification to the desired frequencies.

Because of the very large losses in recording frequencies over 3,000 cps, considerable treble boost is applied during recording. Such boosting begins at 500 cps, slowly rises to 3,000 cps, and rapidly peaks at about 15,000 cps, after which it necessarily drops back somewhat at 20,000 cps. Treble boost during playback would be impractical, because it would also amplify tape and amplifier noise.

Bass boost is normally accomplished in playback, but a small amount is sometimes applied at frequencies below 200 cps during recording. Such boost during recording increases the recorded signal at power line frequencies and reduces the need to amplify the 60-cycle hum during playback. Applying the total necessary amount of bass boost during recording would overload the tape and result in distortion.

Some tape recorders apply half of the required bass and treble boost during both recording and playback. This is an economy measure to permit the same equalization network to be used in both recording and playback.

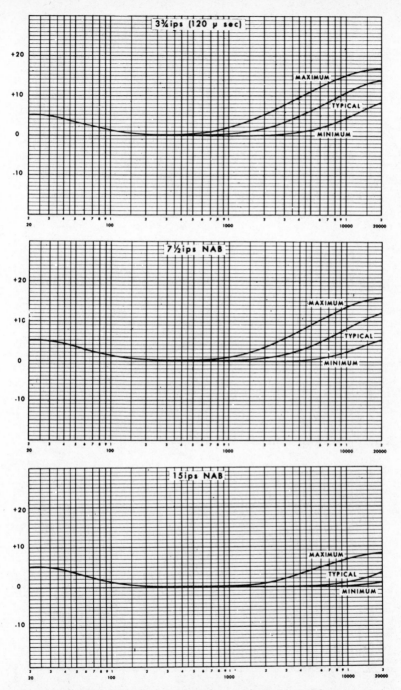

Fig. 6-2 NAB record curves, showing suggested pre-emphasis at various frequencies and tape speeds. Curves are approximate and will vary with tape to maintain flat over-all response. Curve for 3¾ ips is unofficial. *Courtesy: Ampex Corp.*

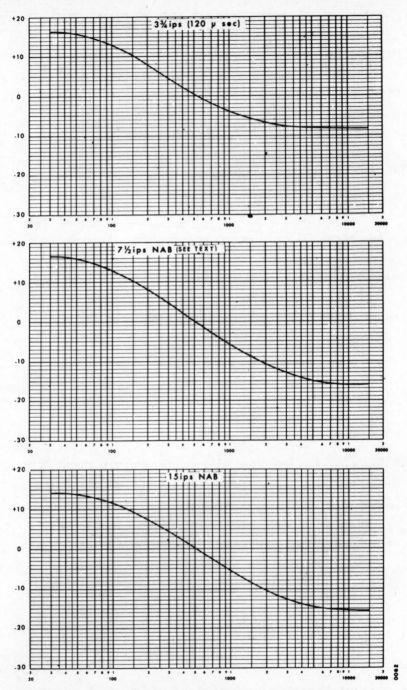

Fig. 6-3 NAB reproduce curves, showing post-emphasis of various frequencies and tape speeds. Curve for 3¾ ips is unofficial. Courtesy: Ampex Corp.

In order to permit high-fidelity recordings made on one machine to be played back on another machine without loss of fidelity, the NAB has established standardized curves showing boost amplitude at various frequencies during recording and playback. Curves for use at 15 ips and 7½ ips have been established, and curves for 3¾ ips are in unofficial use. These curves are shown in Figs. 6-2 and 6-3. (*Note:* Use the 7½ NAB reproduce curve for the 3¾ (120μ sec)/7½ NAB and the 7½ NAB/15 equalizers. For the 7½ NAB/15 AME equalizers, use the 15 NAB reproduce curve.)

High Frequency Oscillators

The recorder electronics system normally contains a high-frequency bias oscillator. This circuit produces a sine-wave signal somewhere between 30 and 100 kc. Two output levels are frequently provided: (1) a low-level output for biasing the recording characteristic to the proper operating point on the magnetization curve (explained in Chapter 3), and (2) a high-level output amplified from the same oscillator and applied to the erasing head.

A variety of bias oscillator circuits are employed in modern tape recorders. Typical examples are described later in this chapter.

Power Amplifiers and Loudspeakers

Although nearly all tape recorders have self-contained power amplifiers and loudspeakers, space and cost limitations usually make these the weakest components. Recognizing this, nearly all manufacturers provide output jacks to permit substitution of high-quality external units. For example, sound reproduction can be improved significantly by using the "external speaker" jack to disconnect the recorder's own speaker and to attach an external woofer, mid-range speaker, and tweeter. Even greater output power and fidelity can be obtained by using the "external amplifier" jack both to disconnect the recorder's own power amplifier and speaker and to attach an external high-fidelity power amplifier and speaker system.

TYPICAL EXAMPLES

In the pages that follow, the electronic features of a number of modern tape recorders are analyzed to bring out both typical characteristics and significant differences. The first two examples are described in extensive detail to assure a thorough understanding of all the basic circuits and their fundamental variations. Subsequent examples describe only major features and significant variations. Some of the examples are the same machines whose tape transports were described in Chapter 5; discussions of their electronic systems supplement these descriptions.

Example 1.   Ampex PR-10-2 Series (Figs. 6-4 through 6-9)

These are high-quality instruments designed for portable professional use. Head assemblies normally contain three (two-channel) head stacks: erase, record, and reproduce. Occasionally there is an optional fourth head of any desired type.

The two-channel record/reproduce assembly consists of two record amplifiers, two reproduce amplifiers, a bias and erase oscillator, and a power supply. Plug-in equalization is available to meet standard and special requirements. The electronic assembly utilizes etched circuit-board construction wherever possible.

General Description. The electronic assembly (see the block diagram of Fig. 6-5 and the schematic diagrams of Figs. 6-6 and 6-7) consists of a single chassis on which is mounted an etched-board sub-assembly containing two record amplifiers, two reproduce amplifiers, a bias and erase oscillator, and the power supply. On the face panel, facilities are available for setting record levels, selecting high- or low-speed equalization circuitry, and switching output circuitry. Visual monitoring of reproduce and record levels is provided by the two VU meters on the face panel. Two phone jacks for aural monitoring are provided on the face panel. A record channel selector completes the front panel arrangement.

On the back panel of the electronic assembly chassis are all connecting and interconnecting provisions for line input, line output, power from the tape transport, and head connections. One screw-type fuse is also provided on the chassis back panel.

Record Amplifier. The two record sections of the electronic assembly each consist of a two-stage, high-gain, resistance-coupled amplifier (shown in Fig. 6-6). Two triode-pentodes, V1 and V2, and their associated circuitry, form the stages of amplification for both channels. To simplify the discussions, only channel "A" — V1 and its related circuitry — will be

Fig. 6-4 Ampex PR-10-2 two-channel tape recorder. *Courtesy: Ampex Corp.*

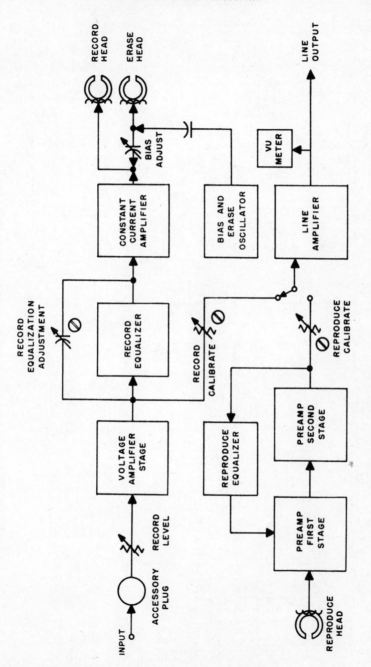

Fig. 6-5 Functional block diagram of electronic assembly in Ampex PR-10-2 tape recorder.
Courtesy: Ampex Corp.

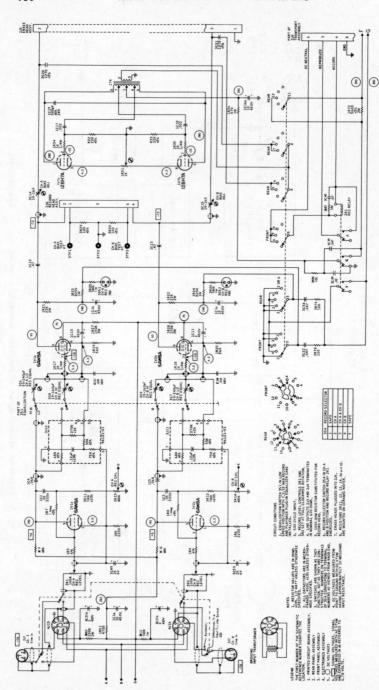

Fig. 6-6 Schematic diagram of record amplifier and bias oscillator in Ampex PR-10-2 tape recorder. Courtesy: Ampex Corp.

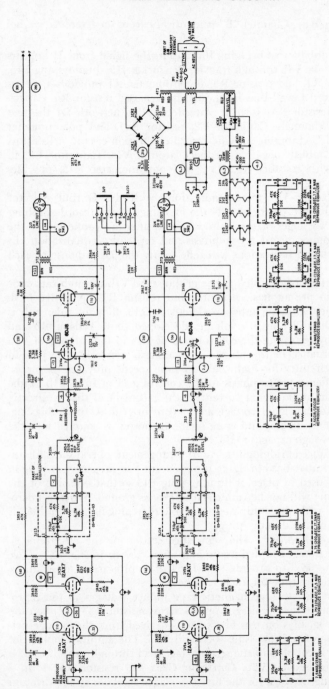

Fig. 6-7 Schematic diagram of reproduce amplifier and power supply in Ampex PR-10-2 tape recorder. Courtesy: Ampex Corp.

described (Fig. 6-8) . Channel "B" is identical except for reference symbol numbers.

With an unbalanced-bridging line input, the signal from J1 appears at the grid of tube V1a through transformer socket J15, dummy plug P15, potentiometer R1, and resistor R3. Potentiometer R1 provides a means of setting Record Level. Bias is attained by bypassed resistor R5. Capacitor C1a and resistor R51 form a plate decoupling network for the first stage of both channels. Capacitor C2, resistor R11, and potentiometer R13 (RECord CALibrate) provide record calibration circuitry. Resistors R3 and R7 establish negative feedback around V1a. Capacitor C2, in conjunction with resistors R7, R11, and potentiometer R13, provides low-frequency pre-emphasis.

When reading VU meter indications with the Output Selector switch in the Record position, only the first stage of the record amplifier and the last two stages of the reproduce amplifier are connected in the circuit. This omits record pre-emphasis and reproduce equalization circuitry so that meter indications will reflect only the flat response of each amplifier.

The signal is now coupled to the grid of tube V1b through capacitor C4, the plug-in pre-emphasis network, and resistor R17. Negative feedback is provided through unbypassed resistor R19. Bias for tube V1b is provided by the difference in voltages developed across resistor R5 and resistor R19, by returning the control grid of V1b to the cathode of V1a through a resistance in the plug-in pre-emphasis network. The plug-in pre-emphasis circuitry for high and low tape speeds provides the necessary high-frequency pre-emphasis to the control grid of tube V1b. Tube V1b delivers an audio signal current to the record head that is directly proportional to the signal voltage at the control grid. A 100-kc bias signal current from the bias and erase oscillator output is coupled into the record head through capacitor C14.

In the balanced-bridging line input arrangement, operation is identical to that for unbalanced-bridging input except that an accessory plug-in transformer is used in place of dummy plug P15 so that one side of the signal input line will not be connected to chassis ground. When a microphone is used with the equipment, an accessory plug-in preamplifier is used in place of the dummy plug.

Reproduce Amplifier. The reproduce section of the electronic assembly is a resistance-coupled audio amplifier (shown in Fig. 6-7) . Two dual-triodes are used to provide two stages of amplification and a single-ended push-pull output for each channel.

Signals on the moving magnetic tape induce voltages in the reproduce head. This induced voltage appears across resistor R37 and then the grid of tube V3a. Bias on this first stage is derived from the voltage network consisting of resistors R49, R47, and R45. The amplifier output of this first stage is coupled to the second stage grid through capacitor C24. Contact bias is used on V3b. Capacitor C23a and resistor R52 form a plate decoupling network for the first two stages. Reproduce equalization is achieved by means of the plug-in equalizer network.

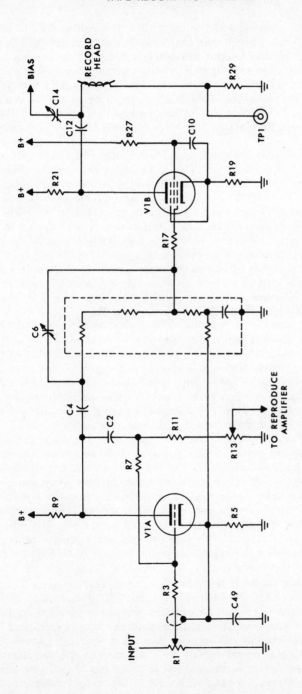

Fig. 6-8 Simplified diagram of record circuit in Ampex PR-10-2 tape recorder. Courtesy: Ampex Corp.

The signal is now delivered to the push-pull amplifier V4, the tube receiving the signal through coupling capacitor C26, Reproduce Level potentiometer R54, and Output Selector switch S2 (when the switch is in the Reproduce position). Operation of the output stage can be shown in the simplified schematic diagram, Fig. 6-9. Resistors RK1 and RK2 establish biases for tubes V1 and V2. With no input signal, the d-c voltage drop across tube V1 is controlled by the d-c bias developed across RK1, and the d-c voltage drop across tube V2 is controlled by the bias voltage across RK2.

When a positive going signal is applied to the grid of tube V1, the tube is driven toward saturation. This causes the voltage at the plate of tube V1 to drop, which in turn causes the voltage at the grid of tube V2 to drop. Since the load RL is coupled to the cathode of V2 through coupling capacitor C1 and the grid of V2 is connected to the plate of V1, a signal voltage drop occurs across RK2 which causes tube V2 to be driven toward cutoff. When a negative going signal is applied to the grid of tube V1, the converse is true.

In the actual circuit, shown in the main schematic diagram, resistor 1R62 corresponds to RK1, resistor 1R60 corresponds to RK2, tube 1V4a corresponds to V1, tube 1V4b corresponds to V2, capacitor 3C30 corresponds to C1, and transformer 3T2 corresponds to RL.

When the output of transformer 3T2 is terminated in its characteristic impedance (that is, 600 ohms), the output level would drop by 6 db if the basic circuit were used. To compensate partially for this effect, 7 db of negative voltage feedback is applied to the grid circuit from the primary of transformer 3T2 to obtain a regulation of approximately 2 db. At the same time, the negative feedback obtains an improvement in distortion characteristics as well as stability of stage gain. Capacitor 1C28 compensates the output stage for flat high-frequency response.

Bias and Erase Oscillator. A dual triode tube V7, connected as a push-pull oscillator, provides high-frequency bias and erase currents. The output of each plate is coupled to the grid of the other triode section through taps on the oscillator transformer primary. Any signal on the grid of either tube section will be amplified in the plate circuit of that section and coupled to the grid of the other section. The signal then will appear at the second plate and be coupled back to the first grid in phase with the original signal. Frequency of oscillation of approximately 100 kc is determined by the inductance of the primary of transformer T4 and the effective capacity across the primary.

The oscillator output is fed through Record Selector switch S4 and through capacitors C20 (for channel A) and C21 (for channel B) to the two-channel erase head. The oscillator output is also fed to Bias Adjust variable capacitors C14 (for channel A) and C15 (for channel B) where record bias current adjustments take place. The bias signals are then mixed with the record signals and delivered to the two-channel record head. Plate voltage is supplied to the center tap of oscillator transformer T4 through relay contact K1B only in the Record mode.

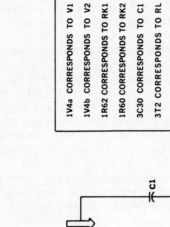

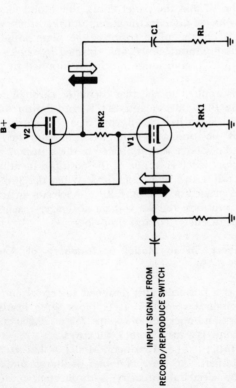

Fig. 6-9 Simplified diagram of reproduce circuit in Ampex PR-10-2 tape recorder. Courtesy: Ampex Corp.

Noise Balance control, potentiometer R31, in the oscillator cathode circuits, is adjusted to correct for any asymmetry in the waveform which would cause distortion while recording.

Power Supply. Silicon rectifiers CR1 and CR2 are used in a conventional full-wave voltage doubler rectifier circuit to supply plate power for all tubes in the electronic assembly as well as Record Indicator lights DS1 and DS2. Selenium rectifiers CR3 and CR4 are connected as a conventional full-wave center-tap rectifier to provide d-c heater voltage for all tubes except V7.

The center tap of the V5 tube filament provides a ground for the d-c filaments. Even though this tube is used only for the reproduction of channel two, it must be in its socket for proper operation of all functions. A-c power input is connected at receptacle J8 and is controlled by the power switch on the transport. The power is fed through fuse F1 and impressed across the primary of power transformer T1.

There are three secondary windings on the power transformer — two for filament supply and one for high voltage. One filament winding serves oscillator tube V7 and the panel lights, the second filament winding provides 12.6 volts d-c after rectification, and the other winding furnishes high voltages for the plate supply. The plate supply ripple is filtered by a capacitance-input choke filter formed by choke L1, capacitors C16b, C16c, and C35; additional filtering is supplied by the decoupling capacitors.

High voltage is applied to the bias oscillator through record relay K1B. Whenever the Play button and the Record button on the tape transport are pressed and when the Record Selector switch S4 is in the "A," "A & B," or "B" position, a d-c voltage is applied to the record relay coil. As long as the d-c voltage is available from the transport and as long as the Record Selector switch is in one of the positions mentioned above, contact K1A holds the record relay energized. When the Stop button on the tape transport is pressed or when the Record Selector switch is turned to one of the Safe positions, the d-c voltage no longer reaches the relay coil and the relay is de-energized and drops out.

Example 2. Tandberg Stereo Model 6, Tandberg of America, Inc. (Figs. 6-10 through 6-19)

This recorder is a portable unit designed to record and play back four-track stero/monaural recorders. It employs three heads, a single-motor tape transport, and operates at 7½ ips (30 to 20,000 cps), 3¾ ips (30 to 15,000 cps) and 1⅞ ips (50 to 7,000 cps).

General Description. The Tandberg Model 6 has etched circuit boards for the amplifiers, the erase and bias oscillator, and the record level indicator. The electrical circuitry is duplicated, compared to a mono tape recorder, in order to record and play back stereo. The main parts are: 2 record preamplifiers for input program, 2 record amplifiers,

Fig. 6-10 Tandberg Model 6 two-channel, four-track tape recorder. *Courtesy: Tandbergs Radiofabrikk.*

2 playback amplifiers, 2 cathode followers, 1 erase and bias oscillator, and 2 level indicators.

A simplified diagram is shown in Fig. 6-11. By means of the push-button system the amplifiers can be interconnected in various combinations, creating a very flexible tape recorder.

Operating Controls. The electronic unit has the following operating controls: A push-button center consisting of 2 record buttons, 2 playback buttons, and 1 start-stop button; a speed selector switch; a record gain control; a playback volume control; and a sound-on-sound switch.

The record buttons are mechanically coupled to the operating lever by the record lockarm, locked in the Normal Forward Drive position, and automatically released when the operating lever is pushed to Neutral.

The start-stop button operates the start-stop relay for the tape movement. It switches on the power to the bias and erase oscillator if one or both record buttons are depressed.

The playback buttons connect the output of the playback amplifiers to the cathode followers.

A complete diagram of the switches is shown in Fig. 6-12. The push-buttons are numbered after their positions on the push-button center, thus: I — record button channel 1 (upper); II — record button channel 2 (lower); III — start-stop button; IV — playback button channel 1 (upper); V — playback channel 2 (lower).

The speed selector switch, which performs the necessary mechanical switching, is mechanically coupled to the equalization switch, which performs the electrical switching when the tape speed is changed.

The record and the playback volume controls both have double knobs, one for the upper track and one for the lower. The sound-on-sound switch makes it possible to record sound-on-sound. The program on one track is recorded on the other track mixed with what is played in.

In normal record and playback modes the sound-on-sound switch has two positions, namely, Normal and AB-test. No interconnection between the outputs of the preamps and the inputs of the cathode followers exists in position Normal. In the first Model 6 recorders, posi-

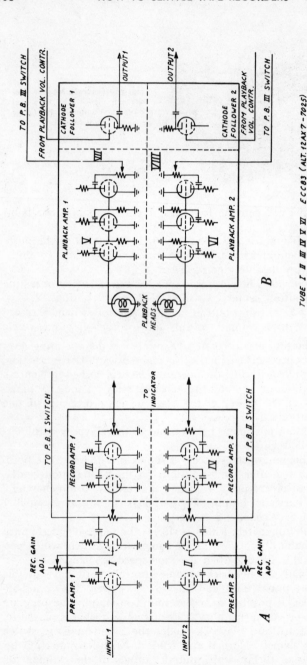

Fig. 6-11 Simplified diagram of record (A) and playback amplifier (B) boards in Tandberg Model 6 tape recorder. Courtesy: Tandbergs Radiofabrikk.

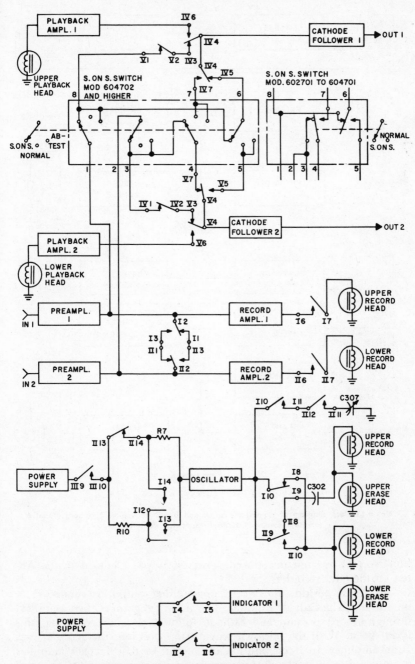

Fig. 6-12 Switching diagram for Tandberg Model 6 tape recorder. *Courtesy: Tandberg Radiofabrikk.*

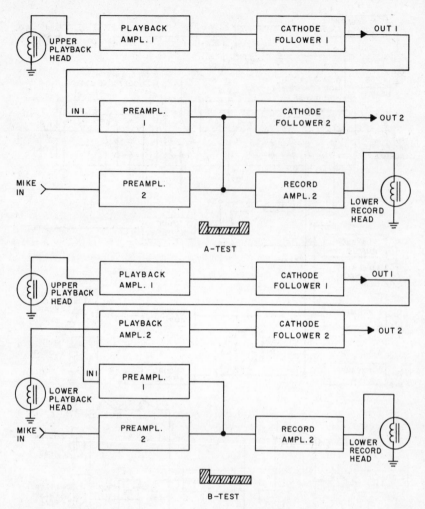

Fig. 6-13 Block diagram of connections for A and B test hookup of Tandberg Model 6 tape recorder. *Courtesy: Tandbergs Radiofabrikk.*

tion Normal was not introduced, however, it was identical to the AB-test on the later recorders.

In A-test position the record preamplifier output is connected to the input of the cathode follower. The input program is then amplified through record preamp and cathode follower. During recording, this is an A-test. With the button released, stop position, the recorder acts as an amplifier. In B-test position the output of the playback amplifier is conneced to the cathode follower input. During recording, this is a B-test.

If the record input of the tape recorder is now in any way connected to the cathode follower output, which may happen in some external amplifier set-ups, a feedback oscillation may occur. Therefore, the Normal position is introduced when the AB-test is taken away, and this prevents oscillation.

The record level indicators are connected to the power supply when their respective record buttons are depressed. The oscillator is energized when the start-stop button (III) and one or both record buttons are depressed. When both record buttons are released, the upper heads are connected to the lower heads through capacitor C302.

In all mono positions, the outputs of the preamps are connected together, that is, inputs are mixed. In stereo, the recorder is divided into two identical electronic units, one for each channel.

For sound-on-sound monitoring on the lower track, the output of cathode follower 1 is connected to the high-level input of channel 1 and the microphone connected to channel 2. The master recording and the mike input will be recorded on the lower track simultaneously. To make an A-test, buttons II, III, and IV are depressed; to make a B-test, buttons II, III, IV, and V are depressed.

For sound-on-sound monitoring on the upper track, buttons I, III, and V have to be depressed in A-test, and buttons I, III, IV, and V in B-test.

Figure 6-13 shows schematically how the different blocks are interconnected in sound-on-sound monitoring on the lower track.

Note that the playback head is located after the record head on the track; in B-test the program played in will be played back after a delay (0.133 second for $7\frac{1}{2}$ ips) .

The Amplifiers. In the following discussions only the amplifiers for the upper track are discussed. The lower track amplifiers are identical with the upper ones.

All the tubes, except the ones for the oscillator and the indicators, have d-c filament heating to minimize hum in the recorder.

Preamplifier for Recording (Fig. 6-14) . Both channels have three inputs: high-level, low-level, and microphone inputs. The high-level input signal goes through the voltage divider R1 and R3. The input signal to the grid is reduced by the ratio 1/27. The low-level input signal is divided by R2 and R3 in the ratio 1/2.7. The microphone is connected directly to the input of the tube. The series resistor in the grid circuit (R103) and the grid-to-cathode capacitance of the tube of the first stage act as a filter for radio frequencies. The radio frequencies are rejected from the amplifiers.

Program mixing is possible through the high- and low-level inputs. Connecting the microphone, however, disconnects the high and low inputs from the grid of the first stage.

The record preamp is a simple two-stage amplifier. A twin triode, 7025 (ECC83) , is used for the two stages. The Record Gain Control, R109, is located between the two stages, that is, the input to the second

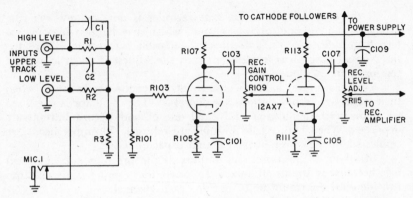

Fig. 6-14 Schematic diagram of recording preamplifier in Tandberg Model 6 tape recorder.
Courtesy: Tandbergs Radiofabrikk.

stage is controlled by R109. The input to the record amplifier is taken from the Record Level Adjustment resistor, R115, in the output of the preamplifier. The Record Level Adjustment resistor is adjusted for highest permissible distortion (3%) in the output of the cathode follower when the program is played back (B-test). The preamp is also connected to the cathode followers through the switching circuit.

Record Amplifier (Fig. 6-15). The input is adjusted by the Record Level Adjustment resistor, R115. The record amplifier is a two-stage amplifier using a 7025 (ECC83) twin triode. The amplifier has negative feedback from the output of the second stage to the cathode of the first stage. High frequency compensation is obtained from combinations of C111, C113, C115, C121, C123, and C125, depending on the position of the tape speed switch (equalization switch). Low frequency compensation is obtained from R123, R125, and C117.

Input to the record head is taken across the output resistor, R137. The center-tap of the output resistor, R137, is connected to the input of the record level indicator. R137 is adjusted for maximum indication for maximum permissible distortion.

Playback Amplifier (Fig. 6-16). The playback amplifier uses the double triodes, 12AX7 (ECC83) (both sides) and 12AU7 (ECC82) (one side). The output of the playback head is connected to the grid of the first stage through the blocking capacitor, C205. An equalizing circuit (C201, C203, and R201) is connected in parallel with the playback head to correct for playback losses at high frequencies. Feedback (positive) from the cathode of the third stage to the cathode of the second stage boosts the bass according to NAB standards. Speed compensation is obtained by varying the amount of feedback (negative) from the output of the third stage to the cathode of the second stage by means of the resistor combination, R217, R219, and R221. The output voltage is adjusted by the Playback Level Adjustment resistor, R233, for a maximum of 1.5 volts out of the cathode follower.

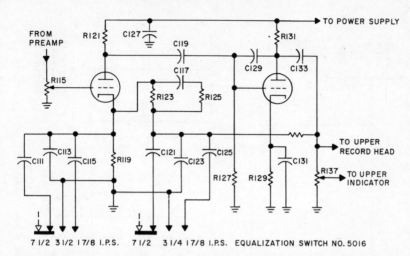

Fig. 6-15 Schematic diagram of recording amplifier in Tandberg Model 6 tape recorder.
Courtesy: Tandbergs Radiofabrikk.

When the operating lever is in any position except Normal Forward Drive, the muting switch is closed and the playback amplifier output is shortened to prevent noise when the recorder is used as a preamplifier.

Cathode Follower (Fig. 6-17). The cathode follower uses one half of the twin triode, ECC83. The input is adjusted by the playback volume control, R18. The capacitor, C225, blocks d-c from the output terminals. Maximum output for 3% distortion from record to playback is 1.5 volts.

The load resistance must be at least 2K ohms to keep distortion below the permissible level.

Magic Eye (Fig. 6-18). The magic eye receives its signal voltage from the voltage divider, R137. The indicator tube, EAM86, is actually three tubes in one: a rectifier, a triode, and an indicator. The input signal is rectified, amplified, and controls the indicator. The rectified wave is "smoothed out" by the damping circuit, R407 and C405, to damp the backward movement of the indicator. The magic eye will close completely at a signal level corresponding to 3% distortion on the tape. The eye maintains its sensitivity over the entire audio range, from 30 to 20,000 cps. The recording current sensitivity is adjusted by the indicator adjustment resistor, R137.

Erase and Bias Circuitry (Fig. 6-19). The oscillator is of the push-pull type using the twin triode, 12AU7 (ECC82). A push-pull oscillator has the advantage of producing negligible even harmonics.

The d-c supply is fed into the center-tap of the inductor, L1. When either one or both record channels are connected, the output across L1 must be kept constant. This is accomplished by supplying the oscillator with the corresponding plate voltages. See II 13-14, I 12-13-14, R7, and R10. The Balance Control, R307, is adjusted for minimum distortion

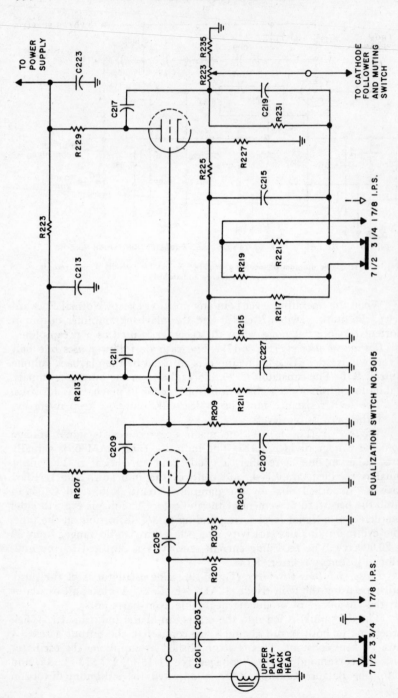

Fig. 6-16 Schematic diagram of playback amplifier in Tandberg Model 6 tape recorder.
Courtesy: Tandbergs Radiofabrikk.

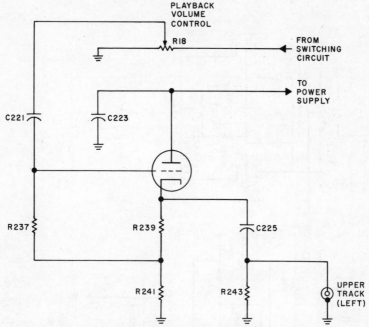

Fig. 6-17 Schematic diagram of cathode follower in Tandberg Model 6 tape recorder.
Courtesy: Tandbergs Radiofabrikk.

in the output (even harmonics). The frequency is set to 78 kc by adjusting the core in the oscillator coil, L1.

The oscillator is connected directly to the lower erase head and through the capacitor, C302, to the upper erase head. The capacitance, in series with the inductance and resistance of the erase and record heads, will cause damped oscillations for switching transients, and only negligible residual magnetism will therefore remain in the erase and record heads.

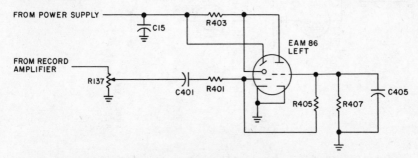

Fig. 6-18 Schematic diagram of record level indicator circuit in Tandberg Model 6 tape recorder. Courtesy: Tandbergs Radiofabrikk.

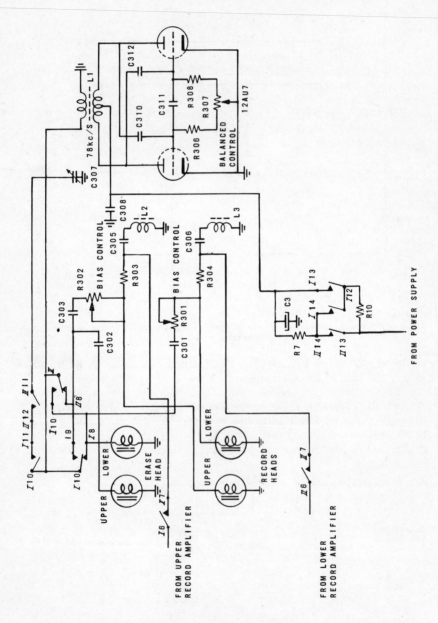

Fig. 6-19 Schematic diagram of erase and bias circuitry in Tandberg Model 6 tape recorder.
Courtesy: Tandbergs Radiofabrikk.

The oscillator also supplies bias current to the record heads. The right amount of bias (50 volts, 78 kc) is adjusted with the bias controls, R302 and R301. To prevent bias current (78 kc) from flowing into the output circuit of the record amplifiers, filter circuits are used; they prevent the oscillator from modulating the program. The components of the filter circuits are L2-C305 and L3-C306. Capacitor C307 is adjusted for 78-kc oscillator frequency with the recorder in stereo position to compensate for the heading by the erase and record heads in the stereo position. When recording in stereo, the magnetic field produced by the two erase head halves is 180° out of phase to prevent unwanted erasure of the track between the two tracks being recorded.

Example 3.   Heathkit Stereo Model AD-22, Heath Co. (Figs. 6-20 and 6-21)

A general description of this recorder and details concerning the tape transport were included in Chapter 5, Example 3. The block diagram of this recorder is shown in Fig. 6-20, and the schematic diagram is shown in Fig. 6-21. Since the left and right channels of the preamplifier are identical, only the left channel will be described.

Playback. The signal from the left channel record-play head is coupled through the Play-Record switch and coupling capacitor C1 to playback preamplifier stage V1A. This stage also provides the proper NAB playback equalization. This equalization is designed to compensate for internal tape head losses and helps give a flat audio response. The NAB equalization network is made up of the internal resistance of tube V1A, resistors R7 and R9, and capacitor C3. From V1A, the signal is coupled through capacitor C5, the Play-Record switch, and capacitor C7 to record-playback peamplifier stage V1B. After further amplification by V1B, the signal is coupled through capacitor C9 and across Record-Playback level control R19. The signal from control R19 is fed to record-playback preamplifier stage V3A for further amplification, and then through cathode follower stage V3B and the Play-Record switch, to the output jack of the *left* channel.

Recording. With the Play-Record switch in the Record position, the input signal will be from the MIC input, the Line Input, or from both. The signal from either input may be mixed with the other input signal. The signal from the MIC input goes through the Play-Record switch, through record-playback preamplifier stage V1B, across Record-Playback level control R19, and to stage V3A. The signal from the Line Input is fed across Record level control R21 and then to stage V3A.

After amplification by tube V3A, the signal is fed to V3B and then to V5A. Tube V5A provides the proper record equalization. The record equalization provides a high frequency boost circuit that is made up of coil L1 and capacitor C19 when recording at 7½ ips. When recording at 3¾ ips, the leaf switch also connects capacitor C21 into the equalization network. This equalization is designed to compensate for the tape

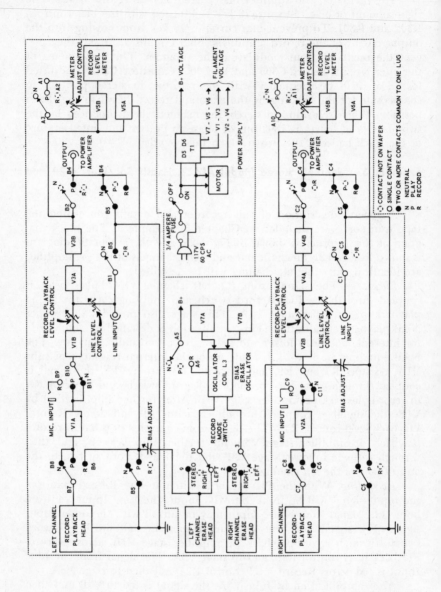

Fig. 6-20 Functional block diagram of Heathkit Model AD-22 stereo tape recorder electronic system. Courtesy: Heath Co.

head losses so that when the recorded tape is played through a NAB equalized preamplifier, a flat audio response is obtained.

The signal from V3B is also fed to Meter amplifier stage V5B and then to the left channel record level meter. Meter adjust control R57 adjusts the gain of V5B so that the meter indicates 0 db for a normal recording level.

The signal from V5A is applied through capacitor C23, across resistor R49, and through the Play-Record switch to the left channel record-play head.

Bias Oscillator. When recording, the 75-kc bias signal is supplied by push-pull oscillator stage V7. The signal is fed through the Record Mode switch and then coupled through Bias adjust capacitor C31, through the Play-Record switch to the left channel record play head. The Bias adjust capacitor allows the bias current for each record-play head to be adjusted individually to the optimum operating point.

The bias oscillator also provides the erase signal to the erase head. The signal is coupled through the Record Mode switch and capacitor C29 to the left channel erase head.

Power Supply. The fused transformer-operated power supply uses diodes D5 and D6 with capacitors C37A and C37B as a full-wave voltage doubler. The voltage output is fed to a four-section filter network made up of capacitors C38A, C38B, C38C, and C38D, and resistors R65, R66, and R67. This filter network provides decoupling and smooths out power supply ripple. Voltage dividers, consisting of resistors R68 and R69, provide bias voltage to the tube filaments of the left and right channels. The filament bias, along with Hum Null controls R71 and R72, is used to help minimize hum.

Three separate filament windings in the power transformer supply tube filament voltages for each channel and the bias oscillator. This is done so that filament hum may be nulled individually in each channel.

Example 4.   Ekotape Series 500, Webster Electric Co. (Figs. 6-22 and 6-23)

A general description of this series of recorders and details concerning their tape transports were given in Chapter 5, Example 2. The Model 500 Ekotape's electronic assembly consists of separate record and playback amplifiers fully transistorized, printed circuit construction, and individually enclosed plug-in type units. These amplifiers are fastened to the amplifier mounting chassis, which incorporates the power supply, all controls, and the input and output jacks.

The Model 510 Ekotape's electronic assembly consists of a record channel, a playback channel, a bias and erase oscillator, and a power supply, mounted on a single chassis. The amplifier is completely transistorized and of wired construction.

Record Amplifier (Model 500). The record amplifier consists of two stages of signal preamplification, a single record amplifier stage, and

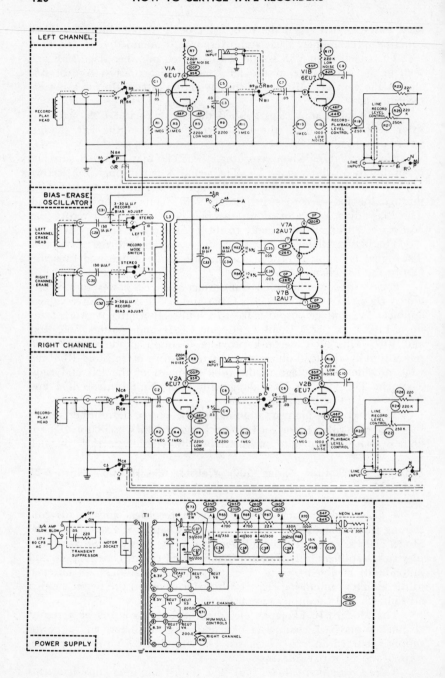

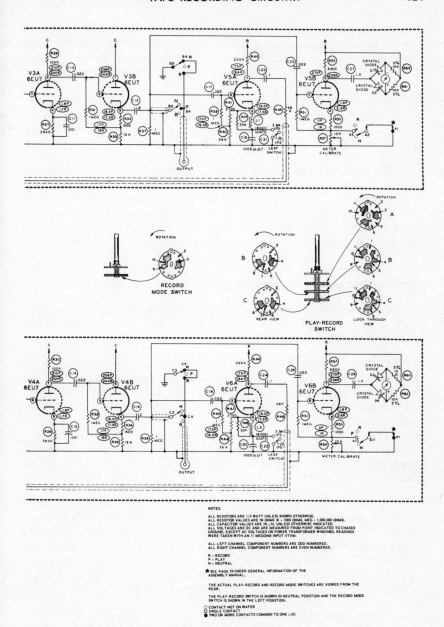

Fig. 6-21 Schematic diagram of Heathkit Model AD-22 stereo tape recorder electronic system. *Courtesy: Heath Co.*

the bias and erase oscillator. The low-level (microphone) or high-level (radio-phono) inputs are fed directly into the first preamplifier stage with record level controlled between the two preamplifier stages. The low-level input is a closed circuit jack that opens the high-level input when the microphone is plugged in.

Record equalization is fixed. The tone control has no effect on the signal fed through the record amplifier. The erase and bias currents are adjustable for maximum record efficiency. Voltage is supplied to the record amplifier only when the Record switch is in the Record position.

Playback Amplifier. The playback amplifier consists of two frequency compensation stages, an amplification stage, a driver phase inverter stage, and a push-pull output stage. The compensated playback signal is fed through the A contact of the A-B switch, through the playback level control, to the output stages of the amplifiers. The B contact of the A-B switch takes the signal from the output of the second preamplifier stage of the record amplifier, through the playback level control, into the output stages of the playback amplifier. This provides monitor selection of the recorded signal before and after it is recorded.

Power Supply. The d-c power supply consists of a full-wave rectifier with a capacitor input and an LC filter providing − 27 d-c volts for the playback amplifier and − 25 d-c volts for the record amplifier.

Record Channel (Model 510). The record amplifier on this model consists of a two-stage preamplifier, a record amplifier stage, a meter circuit, and the bias and erase oscillator. The low and high level inputs are identical to those incorporated in the model 500, both in function and circuitry.

The record level is controlled after the second preamplifier stage, and pre-equalization is fixed with no tone control in either channel. A push-pull bias and erase oscillator is used, with adjustable bias and erase currents.

Playback Channel (Model 510). The playback channel has three stages of preamplification with post-equalization fixed within these stages. Playback level is controlled after the third amplifier stage with the signal from the record channel fed into the emitter of the third-stage amplifier. The third-stage amplifier is direct-coupled to the output stage, which incorporates a 16-ohm speaker and an output jack for the headset. When the headset is used, the internal speaker is cut off.

Power Supply (Model 510). The d-c power supply consists of a full-wave rectifier with a capacitor output and LC filter, providing − 27 d-c volts to the amplifier.

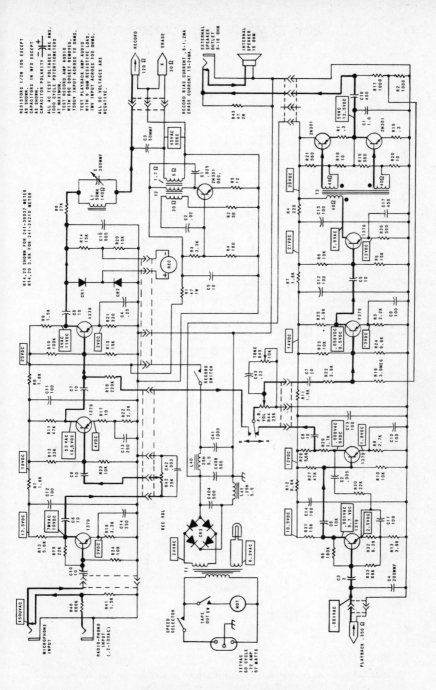

Fig. 6-22 Schematic diagram of Ekotape Model 500 transistorized tape recorder electronic system. Courtesy: Webster Electric Co.

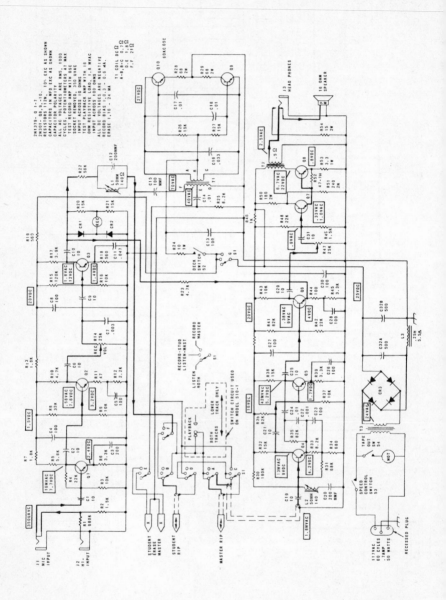

Fig. 6-23 Schematic diagram of Ekotape Model 510 transistorized tape recorder electronic system. *Courtesy: Webster Electric Co.*

Example 5.   Westinghouse Models H21 through H28 (Figs. 6-24 through 6-30)

This line of Westinghouse units is intended to cover all requirements from low-cost monaural recording through stereo high-fidelity applications. Model designations ending with an "S" indicate stereo capability. Unless otherwise stated, all units have two heads and operate at both 3¾ ips and 7½ ips. Outstanding features are as follows:

Model No.	Channels	Tracks	Comments
H-21R	1	2	Self-contained speaker
H-22RS	2	4	One self-contained speaker for Channel No. 1
H-23SE	—	—	Amplifier/speaker to provide stereo playback
H-24RS	2	4	Two detachable speakers in separate case
H-25R	1	2	Economy unit; self-contained speaker.
H-26RS	2	4	Two self-contained speakers; jacks for external hi-fi amplifiers and speakers
H-28R	1	2	Portable, transistorized, battery-operated, single speed

Fig. 6-24 Westinghouse Model 25 single-channel tape recorder. *Courtesy: Westinghouse Electric Corp.*

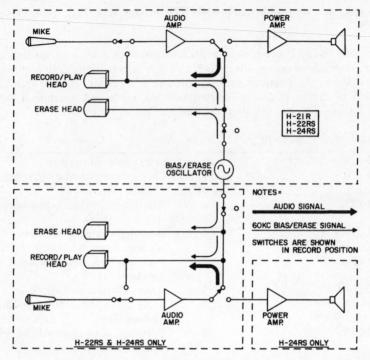

Fig. 6-25 Simplified block diagram of Westinghouse Models H-21R, H-22RS, and H-24RS, showing basic record-play switching. *Courtesy: Westinghouse Electric Corp.*

The outstanding electronic features of these recorders are described in the paragraphs that follow.

Record-Play Switching. Figure 6-25 shows the basic Record-Play switching arrangement used in Models H-21R, H-22RS, and H-24RS. Figure 6-26 shows the complete schematic diagram of H-21R. In the switching diagram, audio signal paths are indicated by a broad arrow, whereas the path of the bias/erase signal is marked by the lightweight arrow.

The Record-Play switch, which is actuated by the Record pushbutton, remains in the Play position during all tape recorder functions except Record. When the Record pushbutton is depressed, a mechanical linkage turns the switch to Record.

When any pushbutton except the Record pushbutton is depressed, the Record-Play switch remains in the Play position and maintains the following circuit conditions:

1. The record/play head is connected to the input circuit of the audio amplifier.

2. The play equalization feedback loop is closed.

3. The cathode circuit of the power amplifier is completed.

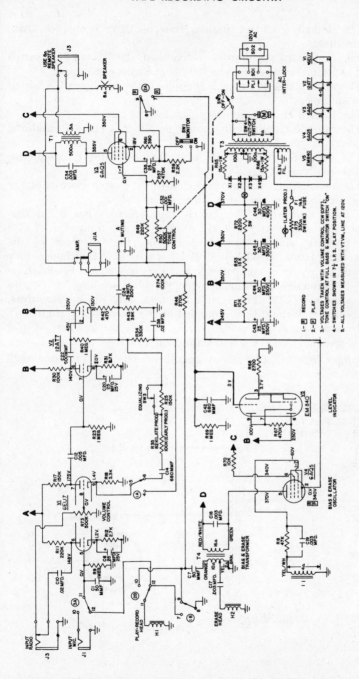

Fig. 6-26 Schematic diagram of Westinghouse Model H-21R. Courtesy: Westinghouse Electric Corp.

4. The cathode circuit of the bias/erase oscillator is opened, disabling the oscillator.

When the Record pushbutton is depressed, the Record-Play switch is turned to Record and sets up the following circuit conditions:

1. The microphone input jack is connected to the input circuit of the audio amplifier.

2. The Record equalization feedback loop is closed.

3. The cathode circuit of the power amplifier is opened, disabling the amplifier.

4. The cathode circuit of the bias/erase oscillator is completed, causing the oscillator to function.

5. The record/play head is connected to the output circuits of the bias/erase oscillator and the audio amplifier.

Bias/Erase Oscillator. The H-21R tape recorder has a "tickler-coil" oscillator, shown in Fig. 6-27. A tank circuit, composed of C18 and the primary winding of T4, determines the frequency of the oscillator (approximately 60 kc). Coil L1 is part of T4, although they are shown as separate components on the schematic. Feedback is provided by inductive coupling between the plate winding of T4 and the grid winding (L1). The oscillator works only during recording, when the cathode of the tube is grounded by the Record-Play (function) switch. In early-production models of the H-21R, the low end of grid coil L1 is grounded only when the function switch is at Record.

Amplifier Section. The audio amplifier section is used for both

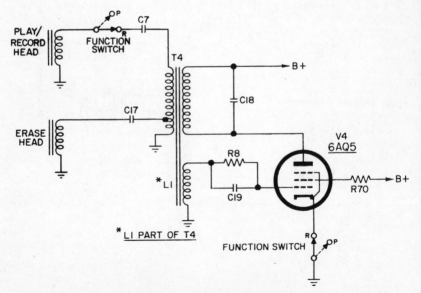

Fig. 6-27 Simplified schematic diagram of bias/erase oscillator in Westinghouse Model H-21R. Courtesy: Westinghouse Electric Corp.

Play and Record (see Figs. 6-25 and 6-26). It consists of four stages of conventional voltage amplifiers, including a "bootstrap" cathode-follower output stage. During recording, a low-level input jack (for microphone) is connected to the grid of the first stage, or a high-level input jack (for radio or tuner) permits high-level input signals to be applied directly to the second stage. During playback, a fifth stage of amplification (power amplifier) is added to drive the speaker. The Tone control is in this fifth stage and functions only during Play.

Equalization. Two separate equalization feedback loops are provided between the fourth and second stages of the audio amplifier. When the Record-Play switch is at Play, it closes the "post-equalization" feedback loop. This network boosts the lower frequencies that were attenuated by the recording process. Because the $7\frac{1}{2}$-ips tape speed requires a slightly different equalization curve than the $3\frac{3}{4}$-ips tape speed, another switch (activated by the speed change control) shunts part of the resistance in the post-equalization network when the speed-change control is moved to $7\frac{1}{2}$ ips.

When the Record-Play switch is turned to the Record position, the post-equalization loop is opened and the pre-equalization feedback loop is completed. This second network is a treble-boost circuit that compensates for the attenuation of the higher audio frequencies in the record/play head.

Other Controls and Switches. If distortion is to be avoided during recording, the average amplitude of the audio signal to the record/play head must be held within certain limits. The average Record signal level is indicated by an electron-beam indicator tube that is connected to the cathode circuit of the fourth audio amplifier. The audio signal is applied to the head from this point. The Volume control, in the grid circuit of the second audio amplifier, adjusts the amount of audio signal that is allowed to pass through the amplifier section.

The muting switch, located under the push buttons, grounds out the audio signal when the Wind, Rewind, or Stop button is depressed.

When the Monitor switch is in the On position during recording, a portion of the output of the audio amplifier is amplified by the power amplifier and applied to the speaker. The switch completes the cathode circuit of the audio power amplifier. The Record signal may also be monitored with earphones at the AMP jack.

H-25R Bias/Erase Oscillator (Fig. 6-28). In the H-25R recorder, tube V2 is the audio output stage during playback, and a modified Hartley bias/erase oscillator during recording. Its function is determined by the position of the Record-Play switch, SW2. This switch, actuated by the Record pushbutton, remains in the Play position in all functions except Record.

In the playback function, the grid of V2 is RC-coupled to the plate of the preceding stage. When Record-Play switch SW2 is moved to the Record position, the grid of V2 is disconnected from the

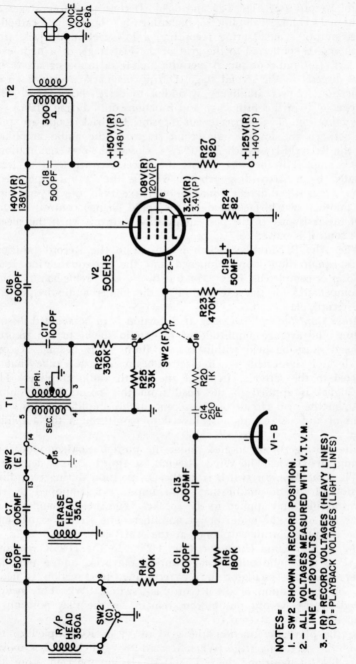

Fig. 6-28 Simplified schematic diagram of bias/erase oscillator in Westinghouse Model H-25R. Courtesy: Westinghouse Electric Corp.

NOTES:

1.— SW2 SHOWN IN RECORD POSITION.

2.— ALL VOLTAGES MEASURED WITH V.T.V.M. LINE AT 120 VOLTS.

3.— (R) = RECORD VOLTAGES (HEAVY LINES)
(P) = PLAYBACK VOLTAGES (LIGHT LINES)

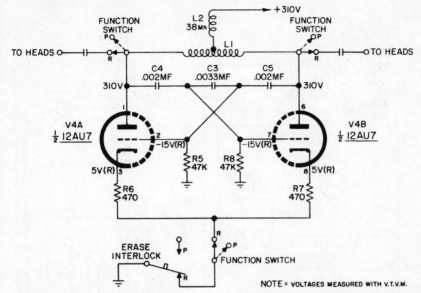

Fig. 6-29 Simplified schematic diagram of bias/erase oscillator in Westinghouse Models H-22RS and H-24RS. *Courtesy: Westinghouse Electric Corp.*

preceding stage and connected to the oscillator circuit through R26. Oscillator feedback is provided by inductive coupling between the plate and grid sections of the primary winding of T1. Capacitor C16 completes the RF circuit but blocks plate voltage from shorting to ground through T1. The tank circuit, composed of C17 and the primary winding of T1, determines oscillator frequency (approximately 60 kc).

When V2 functions as a power amplifier during playback, the grid bias voltage is developed by R23. But, when V2 functions as an oscillator during recording, grid bias is developed by R25 in parallel with R23. Because R23 is much higher in value than R25, an open R23 will allow the tube to function during recording. In the playback function, of course, the tube will not operate.

H-22RS, H-24RS Bias/Erase Oscillator (Fig. 6-29). These models use a push-pull oscillator to generate erase and record-bias voltages. The oscillator is a balanced, plate-coupled multivibrator with a parallel-resonant output circuit. This tank circuit, composed of C3, C4, C5, and L1, determines oscillator frequency (approximately 60 kc). As in any multivibrator, feedback is coupled through C4 and C5. If there is either an open or short in C4 or C5, the circuit will not oscillate.

The cathode circuit of the oscillator is connected to ground through two switches in series: the function switch and the erase-interlock switch. The function switch is a manually operated rotary switch; it is not actuated by the Record key.

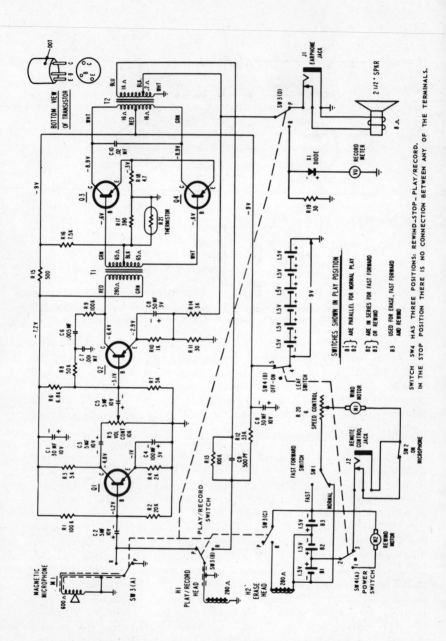

Fig. 6-30 Schematic diagram of Westinghouse all-transistor, battery-operated tape recorder, Model H-28R1. *Courtesy: Westinghouse Electric Corp.*

The erase-interlock switch prevents accidental erasure of tape. This switch is located directly beneath the Record key and is actuated by it. The cathode circuit is completed only when the function switch is in one of the Record positions and the Record key is depressed.

H-28R All-Transistor Recorder. The complete schematic diagram of this recorder is shown in Fig. 6-30. It uses 3-inch reels of standard tape and is equipped with a microphone connected directly to the recorder, a built-in speaker, and an earphone jack for private listening. Battery operation and a minimum of electronic and mechanical components are used to provide maximum portability. Frequency response is 300 to 4,500 cps.

The circuit is unique in its simplicity and in its use of a minimum number of components. A magnetic microphone feeds its audio input signal through two transistor voltage amplifiers. The second voltage amplifier feeds a push-pull interstage transformer that drives the two-transistor push-pull power amplifier. Final power output is 160 milliwatts, which drives a 2½-inch permanent magnet speaker.

Bias regulation for the power amplifier is provided by a thermistor in parallel with bias resistor R17. In contrast to ordinary resistors, whose resistance increases when heated by the current they conduct, a thermistor's resistance decreases when heated by its internal current. Thus, the combination of the resistor and thermistor counterbalance each other's changes in resistance and provide the desired bias regulation.

Diode X1 rectifies the audio signal, thus providing direct current to the VU meter used as a monitoring device during recording. Direct-current bias is supplied to the erase head and to the record head, thus eliminating the need for a bias oscillator.

Example 6.   Star-Lite Model RA-11 (Figs. 6-31 and 6-32)

This unit is a low-priced, portable, battery-operated tape recorder. It employs a single channel, two tracks, four transistors, and operates at a single speed with a high-speed rewind. Dimensions are approximately 8 x 6 x 2½ inches and weight is about 3 lbs. In spite of its compact construction, this recorder provides all vital tape transport and electronic functions. It is included here as an example of a highly simplified type of recorder that can be expected to be in extensive use in the future.

Basic Features. Figure 6-31 shows the outstanding external features of the RA-11. The left slide switch selects either the Play or Record functions. The left rotary switch selects the forward, stop, or rewind tape transport modes. At the right is the volume control and jacks for the microphone and an earphone. Three-inch supply and take-up reels are employed, and there is a built-in, oval, permanent-magnet speaker. The battery case is located at the rear of the tape deck and contains one 9-volt transistor battery and two 1½-volt C cells for motor drive.

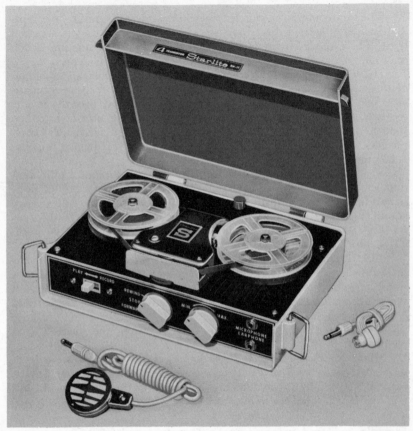

Fig. 6-31 Typical imported, low-priced tape recorder, Model RA-11. *Courtesy: Star-Lite Electronics Corp*

Electronic Features. A schematic diagram of the RA-11 is shown in Fig. 6-32. The motor drive circuit, shown in the lower left corner, indicates the switching arrangement used to prevent rewind when the function slide switch is in the record position. This precaution is necessary because a permanent-magnet erasing device is moved into position when the record mode is activated, and rewinding would erase material that has just been recorded. Not shown in the motor schematic is switching for connecting the two C cells in parallel for forward drive, and for reversing polarity and connecting the cells in series for high-speed rewind.

The electronic circuits are highly simplified. Two stages of voltage amplification are followed by a push-pull power amplifier that is biased by a transistor (Q_{rs}) connected as a diode. No bias oscillator is employed; instead, d-c bias is obtained through R12 and applied to the single head during recording.

Test Instruments

A minimum number of test instruments is suggested for purposes of efficiency and economy. All of the following are normally in the possession of servicemen working with high-fidelity phonograph equipment and are widely available from a number of manufacturers:

1. An audio signal generator (audio oscillator) capable of supplying signals from 30 to 15,000 cps at a stable amplitude level.

2. A general-purpose cathode-ray oscilloscope.

3. An a-c vacuum-tube voltmeter capable of measuring signals as low as 0.005 volt or less.

4. A general-purpose volt-ohm-milliammeter.

5. A harmonic distortion meter.

6. Wow and flutter indicators.

BASIC FUNCTIONAL TEST

Before any servicing can be performed, major malfunctions must be corrected to place the recorder in some semblance of normal operation. Tests and adjustments must be made to bring performance to a close approximation of listed specifications. The basic functional test described in this section will quickly reveal major trouble areas that require immediate correction. Suggestions for making the repair are also indicated.

The basic functional test presented here is readily adaptable to most recorders. While it is important to pay careful attention to the trouble symptoms described by the user, it should be borne in mind that these may be secondary symptoms caused by a significant malfunction that he has not noticed. Performing this test thoroughly will rapidly reveal other troubles that exist.

The basic test is so important that it should be performed *after* as well as before servicing to prove that the servicing has been effective and that all malfunctions have been remedied.

Tape Transport Tests

Before any electronic system tests can be performed, it is vital that the tape transport mechanism be checked to see if it is in approximately normal operating condition. If any malfunctions are noted during these tests, they should be corrected as suggested under the appropriate heading in Preventive Maintenance, unless otherwise specified. Then these tests should be continued through to completion, correcting any other troubles that are discovered. Perform the checks described in the following paragraphs, making any modifications required by differences in construction and controls.

Setup. Load the recorder with tape that has an unwanted sound track. Set the transport to the stop mode, turn on the recorder, and allow a one minute warm-up.

Brakes. Gently attempt to turn the supply and take-up reels in both directions. If resistance is felt, the brakes are in reasonable operation; continue the test. If either reel turns freely, the brakes on that reel require adjustment. Remove the recorder from its case, and check the linkages that make the brakes engage when the stop mechanism is activated. Make any repairs necessary to obtain brake engagement, removing the top plate if necessary.

If the brakes engage but slip freely, check them for greasy or worn surfaces. Perform any cleaning necessary or replace them.

Play Function. Set the tape transport to its play function. The pressure pads should press the tape against the heads. The tape should start to move and be wound up smoothly on the take-up reel.

If the tape fails to move, check to see that the motor is operative and that there is no binding, slipping, or failure to engage in the capstan drive system. Perform any necessary cleaning, adjustments, or repairs.

When the take-up reel does not move or moves in an unsmooth manner, check the mechanical drive from the motor to the take-up reel for breakage, lack of engagement, or slippage. Perform any necessary cleaning, adjustments, and repairs. If there appears to be no trouble in the drive system, see Take-up Clutch Adjustments in the Mechanical Adjustments section.

If the tape rides up or down out of line with the take-up reel, check the tape guides for proper positioning and the capstan for possible misalignment.

In the event that tape spills on the supply-reel side of the capstan, check for breakage or excessive wear in any friction devices in the tape path or supply reel turntable.

Tape Speed. Use the tape speed measuring device to check the speed of the tape at all available settings. Excessive speed indicates a need to check for too much friction in the take-up clutch. Slow speed indicates insufficient friction in the clutch, excessive drag on the supply side of the capstan, or slipping in the drive system.

Tape Position Indicator. Place the transport back in its play function and check to see that the indicator moves as the tape is moved onto the take-up reel. Failure of the indicator to move requires that its drive system be examined for breakage, slipping, or failure to engage. Make any required adjustments or repairs.

Speed Change. Set the recorder to play at its various speeds of operation. Note that some recorders require that the speed change be made with the tape in motion and others require that the motion be stopped before the change is made. Only reference to the instructions or familiarity with the various types of drives can provide the proper answer. When in doubt, examine the mechanism carefully and refer to Chapter 5.

If all the speed changes are not obtainable, examine the speed-change mechanism in operation and make any necessary adjustments.

Fast Forward Function. Place the transport in its fast forward mode of operation. The tape should be moved away from the heads and should be quickly and smoothly wound onto the take-up reel. Failure of the take-up reel to turn rapidly requires investigation of its drive system.

Brake Function. While the tape is rapidly winding onto the take-up reel, actuate the stop mechanism. The tape motion should stop quickly and smoothly with no breakage or spill. These symptoms indicate uneven braking action, indicating the need for cleaning and adjustment. Refer to Mechanical Adjustments in the Mechanical and Electronic Adjustments section.

Automatic Stop. If the recorder is equipped with an automatic stop mechanism, it should be checked at this time. Set the transport to the fast forward mode of operation. Allow almost all of the tape to be wound onto the take-up reel and stop the transport. Place the transport in its play mode of operation, and allow the remaining tape to be wound onto the take-up reel. The recorder should then go completely off in all modes of electrical and mechanical operation. Failure to do so indicates that the operation of the automatic stop mechanism should be investigated and that the necessary adjustments, repairs, or replacements should be made.

Rewind Function. Set the tape transport to stop, reattach the free end of the tape to the supply reel, and set the transport to the rewind mode of operation. The tape should be held away from the heads and should be rapidly and smoothly rewound onto the supply reel. Allow almost all of the tape to be rewound on the supply reel, and then stop the transport.

Failure to rewind in the described manner indicates a malfunction in the drive system between the motor and the supply reel. Examine the drive system, and correct any slipping, breakage, or lack of engagement.

Electronic System Tests

Play Function. Place the function control to its play mode of operation and turn up the volume control. The sound track on the tape should be heard clearly and distinctly. Check the function of the volume and tone controls.

If no sound of any kind is heard with the volume control set to maximum, either the speaker is defective or there is a possible malfunction in the power supply. Refer to the Corrective Maintenance Section.

If weak or distorted sound is heard, there is trouble in the playback head circuits or the playback amplifier. Refer to the Corrective Maintenance Section.

Record Function. Connect the microphone to the recorder, and set the function control to the Record mode of operation. Place the microphone close to a radio that is playing music. Adjust the recording level control for a normal response on the recording level indicator. Proceed to record at least one minute of music. Rewind the newly recorded section of the tape onto the supply reel and play it back. The music that has just been recorded should be heard clearly and with good quality.

If the new music is not heard at all and the previous recording is heard clearly, first try replacing the microphone. Then check and repair the record circuits (particularly the bias oscillator) as described in Corrective Maintenance.

When nothing is heard, the bias oscillator and erase circuits are operating normally. Check and repair the record circuits as described in Corrective Maintenance.

If the new music is heard mixed together with the previous recording, check and repair the erase circuits as described in Corrective Maintenance.

In the event that a reasonably good recording is made but the level indicator does not operate properly or at all, the level indicator circuits should be adjusted or repaired by means of the techniques described in Electronic System Adjustments or Corrective Maintenance.

Any other deviation from a normal recording of the new material requires a complete checkout of the recording portions of the instrument.

Other Functions

Many tape recorders have special features that have not been tested by this procedure and must be checked by an extension of these tests. For example, in two-channel recorders both electronic channels should be tested in the manner described. Also, for recorders having several types of microphone inputs, proceed to check the remaining inputs. In addition, for recorders having several outputs, proceed to check all outputs. Similarly, make sure that all other special functions are tested for an approximation of normal operation.

PREVENTIVE MAINTENANCE

The purpose of preventive maintenance is to assure that a tape recorder that is performing in a satisfactory manner will continue to do so. The process of preventive maintenance includes the routine procedures of head cleaning and demagnetization, mechanism cleaning, lubrication, and complete inspection.

These procedures remove the outstanding causes of wear, locate and correct any wear that has taken place, and effectively compensate for any defects that may result from extensive use. Certain preventive maintenance procedures such as head cleaning and demagnetization may be required as frequently as every 20 hours and are best performed by the tape recorder owner. The remaining procedures are best performed every six months, or even more frequently when the equipment is used extensively.

Although the general procedures for preventive maintenance are practically identical for all tape recorders, the details vary extensively because of numerous differences in construction. Only the general procedures will be presented here; modifications should be made to allow for differences in construction.

Head Maintenance

Cleaning. Particles of magnetic oxide occasionally become freed from the tape and accumulate on the heads, particularly in the regions of the gaps. Adhesive from splicing tape may also be deposited upon the head and hasten the oxide buildup. Even though the deposit may be less than a thousandth of an inch thick, it prevents the tape from coming in direct contact with the head. High frequency response is thereby impaired.

Tape recorder heads should be cleaned approximately every 20 hours of operation. The interval may be significantly longer if the heads are highly polished and tapes with a polished oxide surface are used.

Before attempting to clean the heads, turn off the recorder, activate the stop mechanism, and remove the protective covers from the heads and tape guides. Attempting to work through the narrow tape loading slot results in inadequate cleaning and may exert excessive pressure on the head mounts.

Use only medical-type cotton swabs to do the cleaning. The ends of the wood shaft are completely covered in the medical type and may not be in home-made or economy types. Uncovered ends may result in head scratches and damage to gap edges. Since pipe cleaners contain metal wires that may also scratch the head, they should never be used for cleaning.

Cleaning is accomplished by moistening the cotton swab with alcohol and gently wiping each head until a magnifying glass shows that all oxide and adhesive are gone. Discard swabs as soon as they begin to appear soiled. Note that although many manufacturers recommend alcohol for cleaning magnetic heads, Ampex Corporation warns against the use of alcohol on its heads and suggests a mixture of xylene and 0.1% aerosol, Ampex Audio Part No. 823.

Demagnetizing. Tape recorder heads gradually accumulate residual magnetism which results in loss of high-frequency response when playing back previously recorded tapes. It also increases noise and distortion in new recordings. If playback heads are allowed to become highly magnetized, they may even erase the high frequencies from previously recorded tapes. Demagnetizing may be performed as frequently as every 10 to 20 hours of operation, preferably immediately after cleaning.

Fig. 7-1 Demagnetizing the heads
on the Ampex 602 tape recorder.
Courtesy: Ampex Corp.

Consequently, all the heads and tape guides should be demagnetized whenever servicing of any kind is performed. It is also most important to demagnetize these heads whenever they are continuity-tested with an ohmmeter; the d-c passed through them by such a check leaves them magnetized.

If the tips of the demagnetizer are not plastic coated, they should be covered with thin plastic tape to prevent them from scratching the heads. Turn on the demagnetizer and place its tips against the head so that they straddle the gap. Pass the tips up and down the head several times (see Fig. 7-1) and *slowly* withdraw them before turning off the demagnetizer. Use the same procedure to demagnetize all heads and any steel components in the tape guide system.

Cleaning

Dirt is the chief cause of poor performance in the tape transport and is a major cause of wear. The objective of cleaning is to remove all signs of dust, dirt, and grime without causing damage in the process. Proper cleaning requires removal of the chassis from the cabinet and, in many models, removal of the top plate.

Areas that are particularly important to keep clean are all pivots, pulley spindles, joints, bearings, and linkages. Also of prime importance to keep clean are all components involved in friction driving, including brakes and clutches. All electronic components, including wiring, should be cleaned. The general rule is to search out all kinds of dirt wherever it may be found and then to remove it.

The tools of cleaning are medical cotton swabs, brushes, clean lintless cloth, and alcohol. Begin by using dry cloths to dust away as much dirt as can be reached. A battery filler bulb may be used to blow dirt out of inaccessible areas; air hoses should not be used because they can blow out loose springs and pressure pads and can damage fragile components. Once this type of cleaning has reached its practical limits, wipe all dirty surfaces with a clean cloth moistened in alcohol. Inaccessible places can then be reached with alcohol-moistened brushes and medical cotton swabs.

Since certain components may remain inaccessible to brushes and swabs, partial disassembly may be necessary. Be sure to use compart-mented plastic trays to store all removed parts, and take all possible care to keep parts arranged in the same order that they are removed. If there is any unfamiliarity with any arrangement, examine it in detail before disassembly. Make drawings whenever in doubt.

Flywheels and pulleys may be held in place with locking pins, springs, or nuts. Be careful not to damage these during removal. Then flywheels and pulleys can be gently twisted or tapped from their shafts. Remember that these parts may be heavy, so guard against dropping them with resultant damage to other components. When removing belts, note which side is in contact with the pulleys so as to avoid reversal during reassembly. Some belts have roughened surfaces on the inner side and will not operate properly if reversed.

Use scribe marks to spot all fixed relationships. Remove the plungers from any solenoids and clean them and their cores. Clean the cores of all pulleys and rollers as well as the shafts on which they turn.

Lubrication. The basic rule for tape-recorder lubrication is not to overlubricate. Excessive lubricant spreads throughout the mechanism, holds dirt, and causes slippage in friction drives. If at all possible, carefully follow the manufacturer's lubrication instructions. If these are not available, follow the general directions given here.

Avoid the use of thin oils in the lubrication process. The lightest oil that should ever be used is S.A.E. 10-30 motor oil, and this should be used only for bearings. Also suitable for bearings is Alemite A0-1 (available as Ampex Audio Part No. 71-0181). Pivot points and all other areas where metal is intended to slide against metal should be lubricated with medium-heavy grease such as high-temperature silicone grease, Trojan H2 grease, or R.P.M. Aviation Grease No. 1 (available as Ampex Audio Part No. 71-0007).

The technique of lubrication is simple and is designed to avoid the spread of oil or grease away from the specific area where it is required. Never use an oil can or hypodermic-type applicators. First make sure that the area is completely cleaned with alcohol. In the case of ball bearings use a toothpick to transfer one or two droplets of oil to the ball race. Then spin the bearing several times and examine it. If any dry balls can be seen, apply additional oil, one droplet at a time, spinning between applications, until all the balls are covered with a thin film of oil. Any excess oil should be absorbed with a cotton swab.

A different technique is used in the case of bearings where a hollow cylindrical outer element is closely fitted to, and revolves around, a central shaft. With this type of bearing a cotton swab is used to apply a very thin coating of lubricant to the shaft only.

Medium-heavy grease is used on all metal-to-metal contacts not contained in a bearing-type enclosure. These contact areas are best located by operating the tape transport in all modes of operation and looking for all points where metal rubs or slides against metal. The areas of rubbing, sliding, or pivoting should be lightly lubricated by rubbing them with the greased end of a toothpick or cotton swab.

Take great care to apply lubricant only to those areas where metal slides against metal. Never allow lubricant to come in contact with rubber surfaces or belts. If lubricant accidentally spreads away from the specified areas, be careful to absorb it with a cotton swab and then completely clean away the residue.

Inspection. The period of cleaning and lubrication is ideal for inspection. Examine all friction drive surfaces for flat spots, excessive wear, drying-out, cracking, or damage of any type. Although careful sandpapering may appear to correct some of these troubles, it is only a most temporary remedy; the part should be replaced. Also examine drive belts for signs of wear, cracking, or other damage; replace them if there are any such signs. Glazed spots on belts can sometimes be remedied by careful cleaning.

Examine the head gaps with a magnifying glass. They should be clean and straight with no sign of ragged edges. Any variation from a clean, sharp, almost invisible edge indicates excessive wear, and the head should be replaced to restore optimum performance.

Other conditions to look for and correct by repair or replacement include:

1. Vibration of drive components; check for tightness of mounting components and excessive wear in shock mounts.
2. Worn bearings as revealed by excessive play between components.
3. Bent shafts; lack of alignment and concentricity.
4. Loose pressure rollers and springs.
5. Loose or glazed pressure pads.
6. Loose leverages and actuating arms.
7. Loose screws, nuts, and locking pins.
8. Loose panel controls.
9. Loose magnetic heads.

Certain abnormalities may be detected in the electronic system. Obvious faults should be corrected immediately; suspicions should be noted down for later investigation during adjustment and trouble-shooting. Examine for the following conditions:

1. Melted or charred insulation on transformers or capacitors.
2. Charred or oil-soaked insulation.
3. Loose connectors, plugs, and jacks.

4. Rosin joints.
5. Faulty switch contacts.
6. Cracked tube sockets and tube bases.
7. Charred or cracked resistors and other small components.
8. Loose mounting screws and nuts.

MECHANICAL AND ELECTRONIC ADJUSTMENTS

The goal of preventive maintenance is to remove the causes of wear and damage. Accomplishment of this goal, however, does not assure that optimum performance will take place. Certain mechanical and electronic adjustments must be made to correct any maladjustments and misalignments that may have resulted from vibration, extensive use, and aging of parts.

Mechanical Adjustments

Other than those accomplished during the basic functional test or during cleaning and lubrication, the only mechanical adjustments required are of the brakes and clutches. Various manufacturers determine the need for such adjustments on the basis of torque measurements, which are measurements indicating the forces about the center of the supply and take-up reels.

In tape recorder work, torque measurements are made in "ounce-inch" units. These are most conveniently made by using reels with a central hub 2 inches in diameter. A spring-type scale graduated from 1 to 16 ounces should meet the needs of most recorders. The scale is connected to the hub by means of string or a short length of magnetic tape as shown in Fig. 7-2. Thus when the scale is connected to the take-up reel with the transport in the play mode of operation, the scale will indicate take-up reel torque. Because the scale is calibrated in ounces and is connected to a point 1 inch from the center of the reel, the torque is indicated in ounce-inches. By means of this technique, torque can be measured on either reel in all modes of operation. The

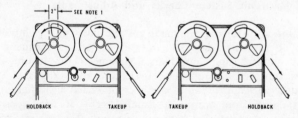

NOTES:

1. IF REEL HUB DIAMETER IS LARGER OR SMALLER THAN 2 IN. MULTIPLY SPRING SCALE READINGS BY HUB RADIUS TO OBTAIN OZ.-IN. READING

2. PULL SCALE WITH STEADY MOTION WHEN MEASURING HOLDBACK TENSIONS. ALLOW SCALE TO MOVE IN TOWARD REEL WHEN MEASURING TAKEUP TENSIONS. TAKE ALL READINGS WHILE SCALE IS IN MOTION.

Fig. 7-2 Technique for using spring scale to measure torque during play (A) and rewind (B). These techniques can be extended to torque measurements in all modes of operation.
Courtesy: Ampex Corp.

scale can also be used to measure the force at the end of the actuating arms and the pressure of various rollers against others. Some manufacturers list the torques, forces, and pressures that should exist at various points in the tape transport and indicate the need for clutch and brake adjustments on the basis of these measurements.

If the manufacturer's service manual is available, by all means use these measurements to determine the need for adjustment. No general standards for such measurements can be listed here, since they vary widely. Many manufacturers determine the need on the basis of functional checks rather than torque measurements. In the absence of the manufacturer's service manual, the "Basic Functional Test" included earlier in this chapter is the best over-all test of the need for clutch and brake measurements.

After cleaning and inspection, perform the complete Basic Functional Test. Make any clutch and brake adjustments indicated and repeat the functional checks until the recorder can pass the complete test.

Clutch and Brake Adjustments. The technique for making these adjustments varies with the type of mechanism that is used. Disc-type clutches have a center adjusting screw that increases or decreases the friction within the mechanism and hence the force exerted by the clutch. Generally, the force is increased by turning the screw clockwise and decreased by turning it counterclockwise.

In those recorders where clutch action is obtained by the slippage of a belt over a smooth pulley surface, clutch force is adjusted by increasing or decreasing the pressure of an idler pulley against the belt. Idler pulley pressure is normally adjusted by increasing or decreasing the length of the actuating arm or the tension on a spring attached to that arm. Depending upon the construction, the length may be adjusted by a screw mechanism, by increasing or decreasing the curvature of a bend in a wire-type actuating arm, or by turning an eccentric at either end of the arm. Brakes are adjusted in a similiar manner.

Surveys of Electronic System Checks and Adjustments

Electronic adjustments are made on the basis of a complete functional test of the electronic system and include adjustment of the heads, bias current, and amplifiers. Any need for trouble-shooting will also be indicated during these checks and adjustments.

Extremely varied procedures are recommended by different manufacturers, ranging from minimal visual checks of head position to extremely complex tests that are suitable only for specific recorders. No purpose would be served by using any of these as examples. The procedures that are suggested in the paragraphs that follow incorporate the most generally useful techniques and can easily be adapted to all recorders. They include Electronic System Checks and Electronic System Adjustments.

Electronic System Checks

In many cases, the initial reason for servicing a recorder will be corrected by the procedures of cleaning, lubrication, inspection, and troubleshooting. Unless the recorder has been exposed to extensive use, conditions of shock or vibration or careless servicing, there is frequently no need for electronic system adjustments. A simple series of frequency response checks will reveal if the recorder is operating at approximately its optimum performance; if this can be demonstrated, there is no need for additional servicing. The described checks are for acceptable response in the Record and Playback modes of operation. Although the instructions may seem long, the tests can be performed very quickly once one is familiar with the procedure. In the case of two-channel instruments, perform the tests in both channels.

Detailed attention to these tests will be most rewarding, because they serve the threefold purpose of final checkout, maladjustment indication, and trouble localization.

Amplifier Frequency Response. Perform this check as follows:

1. Connect an audio oscillator, VTVM, bias and noise filter, and oscilloscope to the tape recorder with shielded leads, as shown in Fig. 7-3. The VTVM should be connected to the external-speaker connecter, and the oscilloscope leads should be equipped with clips to permit the oscilloscope connections to be switched easily between the input and output signal points. An appropriate load resistor, normally 6 ohms at 25 watts, should be connected across the external speaker connector.

2. Turn the bandpass filter on.

3. Load a reel of blank or unwanted tape on the recorder.

4. Turn the recorder on in its stop mode of operation and allow five minutes for warmup. Adjust the tone controls for level (NAB) frequency response.

5. Feed a 1,000 cps signal into the tape recorder radio/phono input. Set the instrument to the Record mode of operation at the fastest tape speed and adjust the input signal to a level about 25 db below the peak level on the record indicator. Using this low level assures that there will be no saturation at the high-frequency end of the band. Mark the setting on the oscilloscope vertical amplifier gain

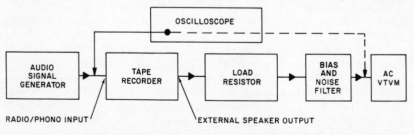

Fig. 7-3 Basic setup for electronic system checks.

or attenuator controls so that they can be reset easily after using the oscilloscope for other purposes.

6. Set the recorder to its Stop mode of operation. Set any switching necessary to make the signal audible from the speaker and indicated on the VTVM. This is the "public address system" mode of operation described in Chapter 5.

7. Feed signals into the recorder at the frequencies of 30, 50, 100, 250, 500, 750, 1,000, 2,500, 5,000, 7,500, 10,000, 12,500, and 15,000 cps. When necessary, adjust the oscillator signal output level so that the oscilloscope signal amplitude remains at the same scale setting. Note the VTVM output level at each of these frequencies, and plot output versus frequency on a sheet of graph paper. You now have a frequency response curve of the amplifier system used in this mode of operation, and the curve should be marked "P/A amplifiers."

If there are any gross departures from the specified frequency response, it is possible that tone controls have been improperly set. Repeat the test with readjusted tone controls until the specified response is obtained. If this cannot be achieved, either trouble is indicated in those sections of the amplifier system used in this mode of operation, or the equalizer requires adjustment. Correct these conditions before continuing (see Corrective Maintenance and Electronic Adjustments).

During the very high and very low frequency response checks, use the oscilloscope to examine the output signal waveform for any sign of distortion; distortion indicates the need for corrective maintenance.

When this amplifier response test is complete, major portions of the amplifier system are known to be in good condition and the tone controls are in position for the following record and playback response tests.

Record Response. The record response test is made with the same equipment setup and general procedures as is the amplifier response test. Proceed as during the amplifier response check, and record the suggested frequencies on the tape. Check the oscilloscope to make sure that equal signal levels are fed at all frequencies. The VTVM output signal can be ignored.

Play back the tape that has just been recorded on an instrument known to be in good operating condition (on the basis of previous complete checkout and adjustment). Use the bias and noise filter and the VTVM to monitor the output of this recorder. Draw the record frequency response curve on the same sheet as the P/A amplifier response curve.

If the record response curve is close to the manufacturer's specifications, no adjustment of any of the recording circuits in the instrument under test is required. Significant deviation from the specifications indicates the need for electronic adjustments and perhaps troubleshooting (as described later) in the recording portions of the instrument before continuing. Proceed with the playback response test once an acceptable recording has been made.

Playback Response. The playback response test is made with the same equipment setup and general procedures used for the two previous checks. Load the satisfactory test tape just made onto the recorder under test, and play it back. The bias and noise filter and the VTVM should be connected to the external speaker output as before. As each test frequency is played back, note the signal level on the VTVM and plot the playback frequency response curve on the same sheet of graph paper.

If the resulting curve is close to the manufacturer's specifications, no additional adjustment or troubleshooting is required; servicing can be considered effective and complete. Noteworthy deviation from the specifications indicates the need for electronic adjustments and perhaps troubleshooting in the playback portions of the instrument.

Conclusion to Electronic System Checks. Significant information has been gained from the described checks. If the previous initial checkout, the cleaning, lubrication, inspection, and the like, have removed all malfunctions, there is no need for time-consuming electronic system adjustments. On the other hand, if the recorder still is not in satisfactory operating condition, adjustments or troubleshooting have been clearly indicated. Thus these preliminary checks serve the threefold function of final checkout, maladjustment indication, and trouble localization.

Electronic System Adjustments

Once any gross malfunctions in the electronic system have been corrected (by the procedures described in Corrective Maintenance), any failure to pass the frequency response tests just reviewed indicates the need for electronic system adjustments. These include adjustments of head alignment, bias current, and amplifier response and are described here.

Head Adjustments. The magnetic heads must be positioned so that they contact the tape perfectly. This requires adjustment of the head height, azimuth angle, rotational contact angle, and vertical contact angle. These adjustments, illustrated in Fig. 7-4, are described in the paragraphs that follow. When making head adjustments, be sure that all tools are completely demagnetized. If it is impractical to fabricate tools from nonmagnetic materials such as brass or aluminum, use a bulk eraser to demagnetize steel tools before making any head adjustments. Failure to adjust the heads as required may result in incomplete erase, erasure of desired material, and loss of high-frequency response.

Height of Erase Head. The technique suggested here is based upon the use of a mixture of alcohol and iron powder sold under the name of "Magna-See" by Reeves Soundcraft Corp. When recorded tape is dipped into this solution and allowed to dry, the recorded areas are clearly visible; the position of the recorded tracks across the width of the tape can be checked with good accuracy.

To adjust the height of the erase heads, load the tape recorder with a 3-foot length of new or bulk-erased tape. Near the center of the tape mark the upper edge with a felt marking pen (not a grease pencil).

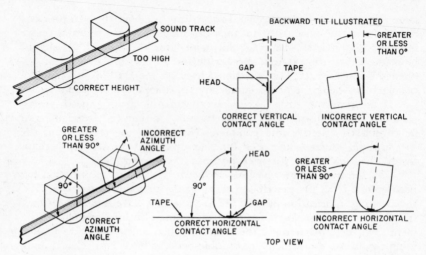

Fig. 7-4 Correct and incorrect head gap adjustments for two-track monaural head.

Set the instrument to the Record mode and the input signal level to zero. This records only the erase head signal on the tape. Proceed to record the erase signal on the tape, turning the reels over as required to record the erase signal on all tracks. Cut a 6-inch length out of the center of this tape (the part with the edge mark), and dip it into Magna-See. Remove the tape, allow it to dry, and examine it with a magnifying glass. The erase tracks should be symmetrically distributed across the tape, as described in Chapter 5 under Tape Tracks. If they are not so distributed, the erase head has to be raised or lowered (as indicated by the edge mark) to bring the erase tracks to the desired position.

Locate the height-adjusting screws on the erase head, and use them to move the head in the desired direction and by the desired amount. See Figs. 7-5 and 7-6 for typical mounting arrangements. Be careful not to cause errors in azimuth or contact angle while doing this, but correct any visible errors at this time. Rerecord the erase tracks, rechecking and readjusting their distribution until they are as required.

Height of Record Head. The procedure for adjusting record head (or combination record/playback head) height is the same as for the erase head. Record a 1,000-cps signal at maximum level on all tracks of a test tape strip. When made visible by the dipping solution, these tracks should be uniformly distributed across the width of the tape and should be distinguishable from the erase tracks. Use the same procedures and precautions to adjust the head height.

Height of Playback Head. To adjust the height of the playback head, first record a low-level 1,000-cps signal on the tape. Play back that tape while checking the amplitude of the signal on the oscilloscope. Adjust the height of the head for maximum oscilloscope output, observing the same adjustment precautions as previously.

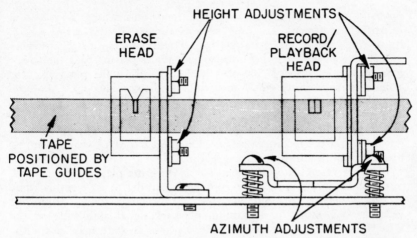

Fig. 7-5 Typical arrangement for adjusting head height and azimuth. *Courtesy: Westinghouse Electric Corp.*

A more accurate adjustment can be obtained on four-track recorders. Use RCA Test Tape No. 12-5-64T, which has signals recorded across the entire width of the tape except for track 3, which is completely blank. Play back this tape while monitoring the output of track 3 on the VTVM. Adjust the height of the playback head for *minimum* output.

Azimuth Adjustments. Incorrect azimuth adjustments at the record and playback heads result in loss of high-frequency response. Since the head gap is not at a perfect right angle to the direction of tape travel, all portions of the gap do not scan the same portion of the recorded waveform, resulting in a response loss that increases with frequency. Although the loss is minimized if the record and playback heads are set to about the same incorrect azimuth, there would still be a mutual loss when exchanging tapes with other recorders. Azimuth adjustments are

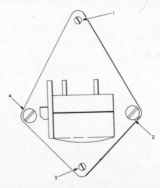

Fig. 7-6 Alternate head-mounting arrangement. Screw No. 4 is spring-loaded and serves as pivot. Head height and forward and backward tilt are adjusted with screws Nos. 1 and 3. Azimuth is adjusted with screw No. 2. *Courtesy: Electronic Instrument Co.*

made on the basis of playing back tapes made on machines known to be in perfect adjustment. Test tapes such as Ampex No. 01-31321-01 for 7½ ips or Ampex 01-31331-01 for 3¾ ips are most suitable for this purpose.

Playback Head Azimuth Adjustment. While playing back the second tone on the test tape (7,500 or 15,000 cps), adjust the playback head azimuth for maximum signal amplitude on the oscilloscope. If the head is badly out of adjustment, several small peaks may be observed on both sides of the maximum position. However, the desired setting will be recognized easily, since it is between 10 and 20 db higher than these false peaks. If the recorder has a combination record/playback head, no further azimuth adjustments are required.

Record Head Azimuth Adjustment. Once the playback head is adjusted in azimuth, align the record head parallel to it. Do this while recording, playing back and monitoring a 10,000-cps signal. Adjust the record-head azimuth for maximum playback signal amplitude on the VTVM. Note that there may be minor peaks, as there may be for the playback head, but these should be ignored in favor of the desired peak, which is 10 to 20 db above the others.

Contact Angle Adjustments. In high-quality recorders the heads are mounted in such a manner that gross errors cannot occur in the contact angles. Wear in the head mounting holes and locating fixtures, however, can result in slight misalignment. These contact misalignments are normally overcome by the pressure pads, which should keep the tape in good contact with the head gap. However, if contact angle errors are suspected, they can be removed by exactly the same procedure used for azimuth adjustment.

While playing back the azimuth alignment tape (with pressure pads disengaged), adjust the rotational angle and vertical angle of the playback head for maximum signal output. At the same time, correct any azimuth error that these adjustments may cause. Then simultaneously record and play back a 10,000-cps signal while adjusting the contact angles and azimuth of the record head to produce maximum signal output.

Bias Adjustments. Incorrect bias adjustment causes loss in high-frequency response, lowered signal-to-noise ratio, and increased distortion. Since the correct bias setting also varies with the brand of tape that is used, the adjustment should be made with the type of tape normally employed.

There is a shortcut method that requires a knowledge of the current specified by the manufacturer. This involves connecting a low resistance (50 to 200 ohms) in series with the record head and ground and measuring the bias voltage across this resistor with a VTVM. Bias current through this resistor is then calculated by Ohm's Law, and the bias voltage is adjusted accordingly.

In the absence of specific instructions from the manufacturer, there are two methods that can be used with recorders having separate record and playback heads. The first involves simultaneously recording and playing back a 500-cps signal at maximum tape speed. While the play-back output signal is maintained on the VTVM, the bias current is adjusted for maximum signal output.

The second, but less exact, method involves the same setup and procedure, but the bias is adjusted to produce minimum distortion in the output signal. An input signal at maximum recording level is used, so that significant distortion will be produced at incorrect bias settings. Distortion is estimated on the basis of the oscilloscope waveform or by a distortion meter. In machines with combination record/playback heads, the tape cannot be played back as it is being recorded; the bias adjustment is more time-consuming and exacting. It requires making the recording with a series of carefully noted bias settings, and then playing back the tape to find the setting that has given maximum signal or minimum distortion.

A grossly incorrect bias frequency also produces faulty recordings. To check the frequency, connect the oscilloscope across the record head. If the oscilloscope does not have precise frequency-measuring facilities, the audio oscillator can be connected to the horizontal amplifier input, and the frequency measurement can be made on the basis of lissajous figures. If the frequency is more than 10% from that specified, adjustment is indicated.

Some recorders have an adjustment for bias waveform. An oscilloscope is connected across the record head terminals, and the adjustment is made to produce a perfect sine wave.

Amplifier Adjustments. Aside from major malfunctions corrected by troubleshooting, there are several amplifier adjustments that can be made as required. These include record level calibration and equalizer adjustments plus flutter and wow checks and verification of acceptable signal-to-noise ratio.

Record Level Calibration. The purpose of this adjustment is to adjust the recording level indicator so that normal-level signals will produce a normal deflection on the recording level indicator; such signals will be recorded without distortion. The techniques for making this adjustment vary widely among the various manufacturers as do the controls provided for this purpose.

If available, follow the instructions provided by the manufacturer. If specific instructions are not obtainable, follow the general procedure outlined below.

Note that the description that follows indicates the purpose of the calibration and is intended as a guide rather than as a specific instruction. The procedures should be followed to the extent possible, making modifications as required by the recorder's circuit details.

Set up the tape recorder, VTVM, oscilloscope, load resistor, and bias and noise filter in exactly the same arrangement used for making the Amplifier Frequency Response Test described in Electronic System Checks. Connect a harmonic distortion meter across the VTVM. Load the recorder with the same Ampex test tape used for playback head azimuth alignment, and set the transport to the same speed of operation. The last tone on this tape is a reference signal intended for record level calibration.

The procedure described first is for recorders with separate record and playback heads in which the signal can be played back while being recorded.

Play the last tone on the test tape. Adjust the playback amplifier volume control to a level that delivers maximum undistorted signal power to the load resistor. Carefully adjust this level until the distortion meter indicates the maximum distortion specified for this condition, usually 3%. Note the reading on the VTVM for later reference, and do not readjust the volume control for the remainder of the test. If the record level indicator can be switched to monitor the playback signal, switch it to that position. Then adjust its playback signal input circuit to produce a normal level on the indicator (zero reading on the VU scale or equivalent magic eye or neon lamp indication). The indicator now shows the maximum setting of the playback volume control that can be used without producing excessive distortion during playback.

Now load blank tape on the recorder. Set the oscillator to inject a 1-volt, 500-cps signal into the radio/phono input. Switch the recorder so that it will record this signal and simultaneously play it back. Without touching the previously set volume control, adjust the input signal level so that the VTVM indication is the same as previously noted. If the record amplifier is in normal operation, there should be no significant change in the reading on the distortion meter or in the deflection of the record level indicator input signal. Then adjust the indicator record signal input circuit to produce a normal level on the indicator. The indicator now shows the maximum input signal that can be recorded on the tape without producing excessive distortion.

When the recorder is of a type that does not permit simultaneously recording a signal and playing back that same signal from the tape, a slightly different, but related, procedure is required. First record a 500-cps signal on the blank tape with the volume control adjusted at a carefully noted series of increasing settings. Then play back this series of recordings at maximum power output. Select the highest level signal that produces no more than acceptable distortion; note the volume control setting at which this recording was made. Then make another recording with the volume control at this setting; while doing this, adjust the record level indicator for normal deflection.

Equalization Adjustments. Equalization adjustments should not be made until after bias and head alignment adjustments have been completed. Set up the equipment as described for the Amplifier Frequency Response Checks earlier in this chapter and for Record Level Calibration, just completed. Adjust any tone controls for NAB frequency response (as described in the Amplifier Frequency Response Checks).

First adjust the playback equalization. Play back the Ampex test tape used for playback head azimuth alignment. After the second tone, used for azimuth alignment, there will be a series of equal-level tones ranging from 12,000 to 50 cps (or 5,000 to 50 cps). These should produce approximately equal indications — within 2 db — on the VTVM monitoring the output signal. Note that since the test tape is recorded across its full width, at low frequencies two-track or four-track playback heads pick up additional magnetic flux at their sides and will indicate a higher output than normal. Make allowance for this effect before deciding that the bass response is too high.

If it is decided that playback equalization is required, make a slight adjustment and play back the test tones once more, while noting the output on the VTVM. Continue to adjust the playback equalizer, and play back the test tones until the desired flatness of playback response is achieved. Plot the playback frequency response curve.

Next adjust the record equalizer. Do this by recording on blank tape equal level signals at frequencies of 30, 50, 100, 250, 500, 750, 1,000, 2,500, 5,000 7,500, 10,000 and 12,000 cps. Play back these signals, and note the output levels they produce on the VTVM. Plot the frequency response curve; it should be within 2 db of the playback response curve. If not, adjust the record equalizer slightly; they repeat the recording and playback of the specified tones and the plotting of the frequency response. Repeat this procedure until the desired response is obtained. The procedure is more rapidly performed on those machines that permit simultaneous recording and playing back of the recorded signal.

Flutter and Wow. Wow and flutter are adjustable only to the extent of the care taken in adjusting the tape transport. The simplest test is to record and play back a 3,000-cps signal. While playing back this signal, carefully listen for the rapid vibrations or coarseness of sound that indicates flutter and the wavering or sour quality of sound that indicates wow. If these effects are inaudible, flutter and wow are at a satisfactory low level.

In the event that extremely exacting measurements are required, test tapes plus wow and flutter indicators are required. Use the indicators while playing back Ampex Test Tape No. 01-31336-01 (3¾ ips), No. 01-31326-01 (7½ ips), or 01-31316-01 (15 ips). Compare the results with the manufacturer's specifications.

To reduce flutter, search for vibration of the tape along its line of motion. This can be caused by friction between the tape and the heads or the pressure pads. Make sure that the heads are all well polished and that there is no glaze on the pressure pads. Check and correct all uneven drags on the tape between the supply and takeup reels.

Wow can be caused by any eccentricity or wear in the tape drive system. While listening to the wow, watch the turning of all pulleys and other components in the drive system. Search for a turning rate that seems to be in synchronism with the frequency of the wow. Inspect that part for wear in its rim or bearing, and replace it if a satisfactory repair cannot be made.

Signal-to-Noise Ratio. Obtaining the signal-to-noise ratio specified

by the manufacturer is dependent upon the effectiveness of the bias signal adjustments, the adjustment of head alignment to assure perfect
erasing of recorded signals, plus troubleshooting and adjustment to remove hum and noise. A signal-to-noise measurement will reveal the over-
all effectiveness of such servicing.

To make a signal-to-noise measurement, use only high-quality tape
that is new or bulk-erased. Set up the equipment as described for the
Amplifier Frequency Response checks earlier in this chapter. Connect
a harmonic distortion meter across the VTVM. While playing back the
blank tape, adjust any hum-balance controls for minimum deflection on
the VTVM.

Proceed to record a 500-cps signal at normal level. Play back this
signal with the volume control set to produce maximum signal within
the manufacturer's specified distortion for such a signal. Write down
the VTVM reading, and note the setting on the volume control.

Rewind the tape and make a recording with the oscillator output
and the record level control adjusted for zero signal input. Record this
zero signal over the previous recording, thereby erasing the previous
recording and adding no new signal. Play back this supposedly zero signal with the volume control set as noted in the previous playback. Write
down the VTVM reading.

The signal-to-noise ratio is the ratio between the first and second
VTVM readings and includes all noise in both recording and playback.
To measure the signal-to-noise ratio in the playback section only, make
the second VTVM reading while playing back completely blank tape.

If the ratios are satisfactory, it indicates a servicing job well done.
If not, compare the over-all ratio to the playback ratio. Little difference
between these two ratios indicates excessive hum and noise in the playback electronics or power supply. A large difference suggests a recheck
of the alignment of the erase head and further adjustment or troubleshooting in the bias and erase circuits.

CORRECTIVE MAINTENANCE

Corrective maintenance, commonly known as "troubleshooting," is
the procedure for locating and correcting the cause of malfunctions that
prevent proper operation. Thus minor malfunctions that can be corrected by adjustment are not considered to be in the area requiring corrective maintenance, since they are normally eliminated during the adjustment procedures. If the malfunction cannot be eliminated by adjustment, however, the need for corrective maintenance is indicated.

Efficient corrective maintenance requires a plan of attack that will
rapidly identify the defective component. Once the defective component is located, it is simply replaced with an equivalent part of equal
quality. Thus, corrective maintenance is most significantly a trouble
localization procedure, rather than a repair procedure. The functional
tests are then repeated to make sure that there are no additional trou-

bles to be located and corrected. As soon as the functional tests and adjustments have been completed successfully, corrective maintenance has also been completed.

Very significant portions of the trouble localization procedure are accomplished by the Basic Functional Test described at the beginning of this chapter and by the Electronic System Checks described later. The first of these, together with the cleaning, lubrication and inspection procedure, eliminates mechanical malfunctions and roughly localizes major electronic malfunctions. The second of these isolates the trouble in either the record or playback portion of the electronics system.

These conclusions can be quickly summarized. If the tape transport does not move the tape through the intended modes of operation and speeds required by Fast Forward, Rewind, Stop, Record, and Playback, the trouble is determined to be in the tape transport. Such troubles are then located by examining the transport in its various modes of operation and seeing where the turning force of the motor fails to be transferred because of slippage, binding, breakage, or failure to engage. With these trouble spots removed by repair, replacement, or adjustment, potential troubles are then removed by cleaning, lubrication, and further inspection, with subsequent additional repair, replacement or adjustment.

The electronic system tests first determine if an acceptable signal can be passed through the public address portion of the amplifier system. If it cannot, there is obviously trouble in that part of the amplifier system. Next it is determined if an acceptable recording can be produced; if not, trouble is indicated in the record circuit portions of the electronic system. Finally, if an acceptable playback cannot be made from a properly recorded tape, trouble is indicated in the playback input portion of the electronic system.

Thus, trouble within the electronic system can be precisely located to specific areas within that system. The paragraphs that follow indicate the techniques for localizing trouble to a specific component.

Amplifier Trouble Localization

Signal tracing is the best basic technique for localizing trouble to a specific stage between the signal input connector and the speaker output. Once the defective stage is located, the trouble is further localized and corrected by considering signal characteristics, by voltage and resistance checks, and finally by trial part replacement. The technique should be familiar to all those with experience in electronic equipment servicing, but the concepts will be reviewed briefly for the sake of completeness.

The specific technique is to inject a 1,000-cps signal into the recorder input. An oscilloscope is then used to check for the presence of that signal at each significant point on its specified path to the output connector. If the signal will not pass through any tubes or transistors, the power supply should be investigated for possible malfunction.

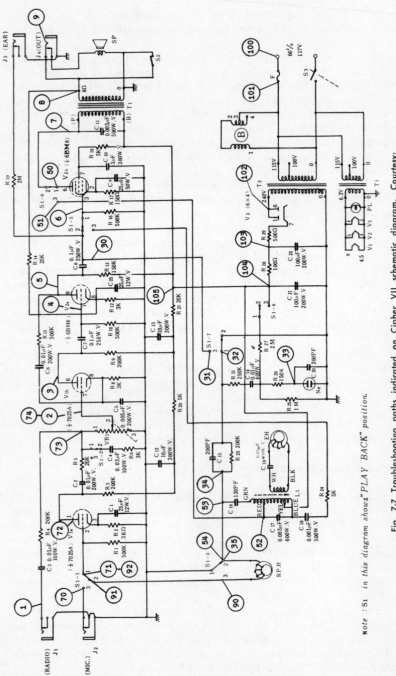

Fig. 7-7 Troubleshooting paths indicated on Cipher VII schematic diagram. Courtesy: Inter-Mark Corp.

Note : S1 *in this diagram shows* "PLAY BACK" *position.*

For example, in the recorder circuit shown in Fig. 7-7, the progression of significant test points is shown by the series of circled numerals beginning with "1" (through 9). Other recorders will have an equivalent path. When the signal passes through a capacitor, it can be expected to come out unchanged in amplitude or wave-shape. If it passes through a voltage divider, it should be expected to come out diminished in amplitude. When it passes through a potentiometer, it should come out lower in amplitude, and this amplitude should rise and fall in an appropriate manner as the shaft is turned. If the signal passes through an amplifier stage, it should come out significantly increased in amplitude. Similarly, the effect upon the signal should always be exactly as prescribed by the purposes of all the various circuits used in tape recorder amplifiers and as described in Chapter 6.

Proceed to trace the signal step-by-step from every circuit input to every circuit output. Stop and look more closely as soon as the signal disappears, becomes distorted, or does not appear as expected from the purpose of the circuit. A trouble lies between the points where the signal last appears as normal and first appears as abnormal. Approach the trouble area as closely as possible from both sides, attempting to narrow down as much as possible the last appearance of the normal signal and the first appearance of the abnormal signal. Between these two points make voltage and resistance measurements at all significant points, searching for defective or off-value resistors, capacitors, inductances, and transformers. Make trial replacements of any suspected components, including vacuum tubes and transistors.

By using these techniques, the defective component will be rapidly located. It should then be permanently replaced with an equivalent part of equal, or better, quality. Then continue to trace the signal through to the output connector, correcting any other malfunctions that are located along this path.

Record Circuit Trouble Localization

If the Electronic System Checks have indicated normal operation in public address portions of the amplifier system, troubles can be immediately localized to those circuits between the record head and the checked-out amplifier, and to the bias oscillator and its connections to the record and erase heads. In Fig. 7-7, the corresponding signal tracing paths are marked with circled numerals beginning with "30" and "50," respectively. Other recorders will have equivalent paths.

To see if there is trouble in the signal path to the record head, begin by feeding a 1,000-cps signal into the radio/phono input. Trace this signal step-by-step from point 30 to the record head, looking for a place where the signal vanishes or becomes distorted or for a place where a particular circuit fails to accomplish its intended function. Use the same localization and replacement techniques as described for the amplifier section. If a normal signal reaches the record head, but no signal can be recorded on the tape, use an ohmmeter to check the head for an open or a short circuit. Immediately demagnetize the head. Also check for the presence of bias signal at the record head. Try replacing the head if there is any suspicion of malfunction. On the other hand, if the head circuits have been checked-out and only a distorted or poor frequency-response signal can be recorded on the tape, proceed to test the bias oscillator path.

In this test first use the oscilloscope to determine if the bias oscillator is in operation. If not, make voltage and resistance tests and parts replacements to place the oscillator in normal operating condition. Then trace the oscillator signal on its path to the record and erase heads. Use the same signal-tracing techniques as before, making any necessary repairs as you proceed. If any repairs are made in this path, perform the Bias Adjustments described previously.

Note that some oscillators will stop operating if critical points in their circuits are loaded-down by the oscilloscope. In such circuits look for oscillator signal presence at the record and erase heads before pronouncing the oscillator inoperative.

Microphone Circuit Trouble Localization

As in the case of the record circuits, troubles in the microphone circuits are limited to very small portions of the electronics system. If the major portions of the amplifier system have already been demonstrated to be in operating condition, record circuit troubles are limited to the microphone and its connections to the previously tested amplifier. When the recorder has an input for a low-impedance microphone, these circuits (and any preamplifier stage) are also included in the area to be checked.

The trouble localization technique involves generating an audible 1,000-cps test signal by connecting a good-quality permanent magnet speaker to the audio signal generator. The microphone is placed close to the speaker, and the resultant signal is traced to the already-tested portion of the recorder amplifier. Signal tracing and repair techniques are identical to those described previously. To check any alternate microphone circuits, connect the appropriate type of microphone and repeat the procedure. The signal paths involved in these tests are marked in Fig. 7-7 by circled numerals beginning with "70."

If microphone damage is suspected, a frequency response curve can be made by varying the audio oscillator frequency.

Playback Circuit Trouble Localization

The procedures for locating troubles in the playback circuit are essentially identical to those described in the three previous sections of this chapter. A test signal is generated by playing back a tape. The resulting electrical signal from the output of the playback head is then traced to the point where it enters the previously tested amplifier. Any necessary repairs are made on the way. Remember to demagnetize the playback head immediately after any continuity tests. The signal path involved in these tests is identified in Fig. 7-7 by circled numerals beginning with "90."

Power Supply Trouble Localization

Signal tracing techniques can be used to locate and repair power supply troubles. The signal that is traced is the a-c voltage from the power line. Well-known changes should take place as this signal passes through rectifier and filter circuits, and these can be seen clearly on the oscilloscope. The signal tracing path begins with the input from the line cord and ends with the B+ voltage at the filter output. Also check for the presence of filament voltage supply to the various tubes. The signal path involved in these tests is identified in Fig. 7-7 by circled numerals beginning with "100."

In the case of battery power supplies, it is only necessary to check for the specified voltages to the various parts of the electronic system.

INDEX